BETWEEN ROCKS AND HARD PLACES

Discovering Ireland's Northern Landscapes

By Paul Lyle, with contributions by Patrick McKeever and Garth Earls

A CIP catalogue record for this book is available from the British Library.
A Library of Congress CIP catalogue record has been applied for.

First published 2010

ISBN 978-0-337-09587-0

Printed in Northern Ireland by W & G Baird

CONTENTS

The vantage point of Scrabo Hill, near Newtownards in Co. Down, illustrates superbly the many and varied uses of the northern Irish landscape over time. The hill is the site of Iron Age settlements in the form of huts. It is now dominated by the Gothic-style memorial tower to the Third Marquis of Londonderry, built in the mid-nineteenth century. Scrabo Hill now hosts a golf course. The former sandstone quarries on its flanks are an important nature reserve and country park, while Scrabo Tower presides over some of the best farmland in Ireland, the Marine Nature Reserve of Strangford Lough and the houses and factories of Newtownards with its airport and modern road infrastructure

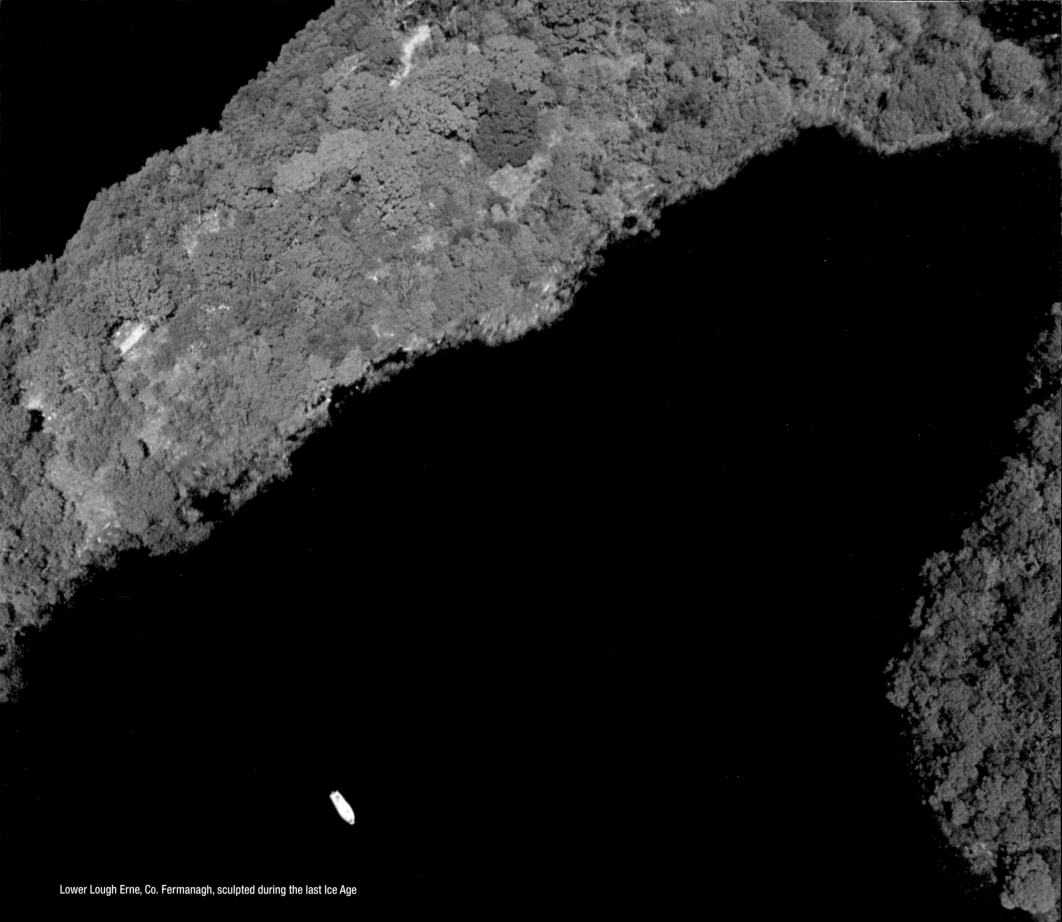

Lower Lough Erne, Co. Fermanagh, sculpted during the last Ice Age

FOREWORD

For its size, the northern part of Ireland has one of the most diverse range of rocks to be found anywhere in the world. The landscape its residents enjoy is the product of the interaction of these rocks with the forces of wind, water and ice that have sculpted them over the millennia. However, some of the greatest changes to this landscape have happened since the earliest settlers arrived after the ice retreated some 9,000 years ago.

Rocks and minerals, the fundamental and constituent parts of all landscapes, have played, and continue to play, a major part in the cultural, social and industrial development of the northern part of Ireland. This fact, I gather, represents something that has not always been fully appreciated, and this book sets out to raise awareness of the importance of a range of geological (and associated) factors, that have not only sculpted the landscape, but have influenced the development of society ever since Mesolithic people first used flint from north-east Antrim.

From this point, use of resources from the landscape has continued, with each innovation inevitably leading to changes in the landscape, often dramatic in extent. Examples of such changes include the use of stone axes in Neolithic times to clear forests thus allowing the expansion of agriculture, or the mining of coal and iron ore in Antrim in the eighteenth and nineteenth centuries. Today's inhabitants are asked to consider how the greatly increased use of the natural resources required for a twenty-first century lifestyle can be reconciled with an increasing environmental awareness that often demands the protection and conservation of the landscape for everyone's greater enjoyment and benefit.

This book thoughtfully examines the fascinating relationships between the many factors contributing to the state of the present-day landscape and the influence of the physical landscape on the residents of the northern part of Ireland, from the earliest settlers to the diverse population currently occupying the area for what is a small portion of geological time.

Between Rocks and Hard Places deals with a range of geological concepts and ideas in an accessible way and has numerous interesting facts and figures that will hopefully cause the reader to reflect on a small piece of history – both in time and place. In this way it will engage members of the general public who are interested in the landscape around them and will enhance their appreciation of this unique area.

Iain Stewart
Professor of Geosciences
Communication
University of Plymouth

Magilligan Point and Benone, Co. Londonderry, shaped by the power of wind and ocean currents

ACKNOWLEDGEMENTS

I am pleased to acknowledge the part played by colleagues and others who gave freely of their time and advice during the production of this book. Garth Earls, as Director of the Geological Survey of Northern Ireland, was the inspiration behind the project and he and Patrick McKeever have made significant contributions to the text. Alex Donald and Mike Young provided valuable technical and administrative support.

The book has benefited greatly from the editorial and design endeavours of Michael Johnston (Editorial Solutions Ltd) and Leslie Stannage (Leslie Stannage Design), and I thank them for their attention to detail and their tact and patience. Michael Hughes and Marie Maguire from TSO played a significant role in keeping all sides of the operation in touch with one another and ensured we finished the project successfully and on schedule.

All of the above were members of the editorial committee whose deliberations, often prolonged but always constructive, helped to improve the content and cohesion of the book. My thanks to the staff of the National Museums of Northern Ireland, particularly Peter Crowther and Kenneth James, for their help in sourcing crucial illustrations and specimens, and to Brian McConnell of the Geological Survey of Ireland who provided valuable assistance with aspects of the geology of Donegal.

Support and constructive comments from John Arthurs, Tony Bazley, Edward and Isa Ferguson, John Fulton, Iris Lyle and Gary and Rachel Smylie, have been beneficial to the whole project and are greatly appreciated.

Finally I would like to thank my wife, Sylvia Lyle, for her constant and unflagging help and encouragement from the beginning of this undertaking, including her detailed comments on the early drafts of the text. I am also grateful for her company during the fieldwork in a variety of weather conditions, not all of them conducive to comfort.

Dr Paul Lyle

The columnar basalts of the Giant's Causeway, Co. Antrim

A SPECTACULAR INHERITANCE

Although taking up a mere 0.0054% of the total area of planet Earth, the inhabitants of Ireland's northern landscapes are blessed with some of the most spectacular scenery to be found anywhere in the world. Primarily, this is due to the rich diversity and age of the rock types that form the breathtaking coastlines, mountains, loughs, rivers and landscapes: in other words, its geology.

For its size, there is as great a range of rock types and rock ages in the northern third of Ireland as you can find anywhere else in Europe and indeed further afield. To the envy of many, within this small space it is possible to see and examine rocks across almost the entire range of geological time.

In some parts of the world, an area the size of this region might consist of one single and unvaried type of rock. Yet, to the northern landscapes of Ireland geological fate has bequeathed stunning natural wonders such as the Giant's Causeway and the Marble Arch Caves, as well as a host of outstanding panoramas, vistas and views in a land rich with folklore, myth and legend.

Between its rocks and hard places, and amid its beauty and diversity, the landscape has always exerted a strong influence on the social, cultural and industrial development of the people of the island. Indeed most of the main developments that have happened in Ireland are in some way due to its geology.

For example, the early dwellers on the island discovered how to use natural geological resources such as flint and iron ore to develop and expand agriculture, early culture and society. Then they integrated the landscape into rituals, ceremonies, mythologies and other cultural activities. It is apparent they had, if not a firm grasp of geological principles, then a profound appreciation of the various components of the landscape they inherited.

The early inhabitants must have seen too, as we see today, that Ireland's northern lands exhibit a number of distinctive natural regions that differ, contrast and complement each other, yet evoke strong

> **" Civilisation exists by geological consent, subject to change without notice. "**
>
> **Will Durant**
> **American writer, historian and philosopher**

and individual senses of place. They will have been familiar with the landscape's varied and impressive mix of upland, lowland, rivers, lakes and seashores. It provided then, as it does now, the arena for life, influencing the food we eat, the water we drink, the styles of our architecture and the material that paves our roads.

The peculiar rock formations, the strange shaped mountains and hills, and mysterious springs and wells have intrigued us for generations, and this has helped to create a land of legend, indeed a mythological inheritance that is among the richest in the world. Today, with our scientific knowledge, we have detailed

explanations for our landscape features and phenomena. But it wasn't always so. The people of earlier times also looked for explanations. And without knowledge of the complex workings of the planet, they developed a series of myths, legends and beliefs about their land: that it was supernatural, that it was a testament to earlier inhabitants, that it proved the existence of the *Sídhe*, or fairy-folk. As a result many special places in our landscape became associated with the great mythological heroes of Irish society or the religious rites of the Celts and earlier peoples. Later, when Christianity arrived in Ireland, it adopted many of these sites and a large number are still strongly associated with the particular

The spectacular sea cliffs at Slieve League, Co. Donegal, are among the highest in Europe at over 500 m

MYTHOLOGY AND GEOLOGY

Sunrise at Torr Head, Co. Antrim. The rocks here are a direct continuation of those that form the Scottish Highlands

The Children of Lír

Torr Head, a windswept crag of ancient schists and limestones from over 600 million years ago, overlooks the wild waters of the Sea of Moyle, the shortest stretch of water between Northern Ireland and Scotland. Legend has it that the four Children of Lír, turned into swans by their evil stepmother Aoife, had to suffer 300 years on these treacherous seas, having already spent 300 years on Lough Derravarragh in Co. Westmeath. It was only after a further 300 years at Inishglora in Co. Clare that their curse ended. While the children were swans, Saint Patrick converted Ireland to Christianity. As the swans turned back into human form, they quickly got baptised before turning into 900 year-old, wretched, aged forms and dying.

Fair Head on the north Antrim coast from Rathlin Island – for invaders like the Vikings arriving from the north this would have been among the first views of the island of Ireland

blend of Christianity and Celtic spirituality that is unique to Ireland.

People call it the land of saints and scholars, the land of myth and legend, the land of a hundred thousand welcomes, the land of the heart's desire and dozens of other descriptions that strive to capture its essence and magnificence. The landscape remains one of the biggest influences on our cultural lives – on music, literature, art and even on our psyche. In music, for instance, the impact of innumerable mountains, hills, rivers, valleys, villages and towns throughout the region is celebrated in an equally countless number of traditional tunes, airs and folk songs. The works of hundreds of Irish visual artists such as TP Flanagan and Paul Henry, and world-famous poets like William Butler Yeats, Seamus Heaney, Michael Longley and Patrick

Kavanagh have drawn inspiration from the landscapes in Co. Fermanagh, Co. Sligo, Co. Mayo, Co. Londonderry, Co. Monaghan and elsewhere. In modern times novelist and broadcaster Sam Hanna Bell depicted rural life in Co. Down settings, while modern fiction writer John McGahern's prose evokes the hills and lakes of south Ulster.

And so we cannot escape landscape. It affects all of us in some way. Consciously and subconsciously we acknowledge its beauty and drama, its changing colours and subtle moods and affiliations.

Time and erosion have taken much away from the original pristine landscape that emerged after the close of the last Ice Age 13,000 years ago, and human activity has added much to it since. But the evidence and the influence of

the spectacular geological inheritance of the northern portion of Ireland lie all around us.

The Antrim Plateau

Among the geological treasures of the Antrim Plateau are the famous Antrim Coast and Glens, a designated area of outstanding natural beauty, and the Giant's Causeway, a UNESCO (United Nations Educational, Scientific and Cultural Organisation) World Heritage Site. It is little wonder the north-east region is regarded as one of the most spectacular and scenic parts of Ireland.

Peaking at Trostan, at a height of 554 m, this upland region descends steeply to form the renowned nine Glens of Antrim, cut by fast flowing rivers running east and north-east towards the sea. The plateau region also features a series of gentle bays and valleys, dramatic headlands, farmland, and a wild and untouched upland blanket bog, the Garron Plateau. Meanwhile, Rathlin Island, Northern Ireland's only inhabited offshore island, lies 10 km off the coast at Ballycastle and is composed of the same rock types as the mainland.

The dark basalt rocks that dominate the Antrim Plateau erupted onto its surface as lava around 60 million years ago when the North American and European continents were in the throes of splitting away from each other to form the North Atlantic Ocean. At this time north-east Ireland would have looked much as Iceland does today, with dark piles of volcanic ash and active volcanoes scattered about the countryside. The basalt lavas covered a land surface that was mainly white limestone or chalk.

Chalk deposits have disappeared from most of Ireland over the millennia, but chalk survives in Co. Antrim because the lava covering protected it from erosion. The soft chalk, composed of the skeletons of microscopic fossils, formed on the floor of a shallow but extensive sea that had covered much of northern and central Europe during what was one of the Earth's high sea-level periods, with the water as much as 200 m higher than today. When global sea levels lowered, the area reverted to a chalky land surface and the scene was set for the cataclysmic eruptions that built the Antrim Plateau. We know that the early stages of this process were explosive, because the cliffs at nearby Carrick-a-Rede are formed of ash and boulders thrown out by the enormous power of an erupting volcano.

At a later stage a large body of lava about 100 m deep formed in what is now north Antrim, and its slow cooling, probably while its surface was flooded, gave time for the rock to arrange itself into the unique patterns found at the Giant's Causeway (see page 28).

The Great Arch at the White Rocks, near Portrush, Co. Antrim. These sea cliffs are Antrim's equivalent of the White Cliffs of Dover

MYTHOLOGY AND GEOLOGY

The Giant's Causeway, Co. Antrim – a similar formation is to be found at Fingal's Cave on the island of Staffa in the Inner Hebrides

No cause for Finn to take the coward's way

The geology of the Antrim Plateau reaches its zenith at the amazing hexagonal columns of basalt lava at the Giant's Causeway. Its very name links our geological and mythological heritages. The giant in question is none other than Finn McCool (Fionn Mac Cumhail), the foremost hero of Irish mythology. Stories and tales of his superhuman power and strength abound.

Most stories about Finn bear no resemblance to his cowardly portrayal in the Giant's Causeway tale, and the original name of the site suggests previous generations did not associate Finn with these strange rocks at all. The original name of the site was Clochan na bhFómarach, meaning 'the stones of the Fomorians', and it was considered that these strange rocks were among the last visible remnants of that vanished race, earlier inhabitants of Ireland defeated by the incoming Tuatha Dé Dannan.

The present day association with Finn McCool may be a relatively recent invention. It suggests Finn built the causeway as a path across to Scotland to fight Benandonner, his Scottish counterpart. It is said he fell asleep before finding his enemy, but later Benandonner came looking for Finn. Seeing that he would be no match for Benandonner, Finn's wife quickly got her husband to dress as a baby, put him in a cradle and give him a steak to chew on. When Benandonner saw the 'baby' he fled. For if Finn's baby was already that size, how big would the man himself be?

The Cave Hill, Co. Antrim, overlooks Belfast and Belfast Lough and marks the southern edge of the basalt lavas that erupted about 60 million years ago and form the Antrim Plateau

When the eruptions ended, the former volcanoes and volcanic centres were quickly eroded to leave behind 'volcanic plugs'. A volcanic plug is a landform created when molten rock hardens within the 'throat' or vent of an active volcano. Erosion removes the outer layers of the volcano to leave behind the hardened 'heart' as a prominent feature on the landscape. Slemish, in mid-Antrim, is the biggest of a number of volcanic plugs on and around the Antrim Plateau.

Overlooking Belfast to the north and west, the Belfast Hills mark the south-eastern edge of these lava flows from 60 million years ago. However, the basalt is visible everywhere in Co. Antrim, from the River Bann, eastwards to the Antrim Coast, and southwards to the Lagan Valley.

With a long settlement history and associated archaeological sites, historic monuments, listed buildings and conservation areas, the Antrim Plateau is rich in folklore with a strong cultural heritage and close associations with Scotland.

The Donegal Highlands and Sperrin Mountains

The Donegal Highlands and Sperrin Mountains, celebrated among poets, writers, hikers and tourists alike for their breathtaking and rugged scenery, cover parts of Co. Donegal, Co. Londonderry and Co. Tyrone and are formed from rocks more than 420 million years old, including some of the oldest in Ireland.

The rocks of the Donegal Highlands and Sperrins are an extension of the Highlands of Scotland and Norway and they also occur on the north-east coast of Antrim around Torr Head. These rocks are the remains of the Caledonian Mountains, a magnificent ancient mountain range that geologists have established was once higher and more extensive than the present-day Himalayas (see page 18).

Typical of the type of landform produced by these very old metamorphic rocks is the distinctive peak of Errigal, the highest and most spectacular point in Donegal. Errigal is composed of quartzite, a rock consisting almost entirely of quartz grains. These were derived from beach sands on the margins of an ocean that existed over 470 million years ago (see page 20). This ocean disappeared when continents on either side of it came together and collided, pushing up the Caledonian Mountains and transforming the former beach sands into hard quartzite. Today the mountains of Donegal and the Sperrins are evidently not the height of the Himalayas. The reason is erosion. Errigal and other impressive peaks such as Muckish, also in north

MYTHOLOGY AND GEOLOGY

The Giant's Stone, Eskeradooey, Co. Tyrone

The Giant's Stone

To the west of Gortin in the heart of the Sperrins in Co.Tyrone is a hillside that was once the home of two giants. The giants were not on friendly terms and were often heard hurling abuse and insults at each other. Sometimes they would even hurl huge stones at each other. Today, almost all of the stones have disappeared – except for one. You can still see it today near Eskeradooey and it is known locally as the Giant's Stone (in fact it is a Bronze Age standing stone).

The Glenelly Valley, Co. Tyrone, forms part of a chain of very old rocks that link the Highlands of Scotland with the Donegal Highlands

Donegal, are only the eroded roots of this massive mountain range.

The other dominant rock type in the region, occurring in the central and northern part of Donegal, is granite. These rocks formed from the partial melting of the Earth's outermost solid shell, or crust, as continents collided around 420–470 million years ago. The Poisoned Glen at Dún Luiche, an ice-sculpted valley with a u-shaped profile and rounded surfaces, is a fine example of the granite landscape of central Donegal.

The Sperrins, another designated area of outstanding natural beauty, form parts of the counties of Tyrone and Londonderry, and are the oldest and most extensive highland area of Northern Ireland.

Reaching almost 700 m, these mountains are less steep and more rounded than the Donegal Highlands, the Mournes or the Antrim hills. The Ice Age, which ended only 13,000 years ago, blanketed the Sperrins in ice, creating their rounded profile we see today.

The distinctive peak of Errigal in Co. Donegal is composed of the rock quartzite, seen here in the foreground of the picture

MYTHOLOGY AND GEOLOGY

Lough Finn, Co. Donegal, is a good example of the long and narrow loughs formed by glaciers gouging across the countryside, leaving behind characteristic u-shape valleys

The naming of Lough Finn

Long and deep, Lough Finn in Co. Donegal is typical of lakes in glaciated valleys. Loch Ness in Scotland is another example and, of course, is associated with the famous Loch Ness Monster. Not to be outdone, Lough Finn has its own story: a young huntsman known as Feardhomhain was once on his way home after hunting with the Fianna. He encountered a fearsome boar that often frequented the area near the lake.

With his three hunting dogs he resolved to put an end to this much-feared boar. However, the dogs were no match for the monster and after they were dead, it turned its attention to Feardhomhain. He fought bravely, retreating up the length of the lough. As the beast began to overpower him, he called out for his beloved sister who picked up her sword and came quickly.

But the echoes in the steep and confined valley confused the girl and she couldn't tell exactly where the cries of help were coming from. She swam across the lake only to swim back to the other side. Confused, she again jumped into the waters. But this time her hair fell loose and became entangled with her feet and her sword. Unable to free herself and weighed down by her own sword, the young girl drowned. Her name was Finngheal and she gave her name to the lough – Finn.

MYTHOLOGY AND GEOLOGY

The celebrated flat-topped profile of Benbulben, Co. Sligo, is caused by the nearly horizontal layers of limestone making up the mountain

Diarmuid and Gráinne

The almost horizontal layers of limestone, sandstone and mudstone in this area have given us a landscape characterised by table-topped mountains. Lauded for its beauty, it is no surprise that it is also the dramatic setting for the story of Diarmuid and Gráinne, the tragic heroes of one of Ireland's most famous love stories. Gráinne was the daughter of the High King and betrothed to Finn McCool. But she met and fell in love with Finn's friend Diarmuid Ó Duibhne, whom she forced to elope with her. Finn was enraged and chased the couple all over the country until, after many years, he made peace with them. The couple settled near Ballymote.

One night the sound of barking dogs awakened Diarmuid. On investigating, he found Finn and the Fianna on Benbulben hunting a boar that had killed 50 of their men. Just at that moment, the boar appeared and Diarmuid drove his sword into the animal, killing it, but not before its tusk pierced his side. As he lay dying, Diarmuid pleaded with Finn to use his supernatural powers to heal him by letting him drink water from his hands. But, remembering his humiliation at the hands of Diarmuid, Finn allowed the water to slip through his fingers. Feeling the hard stares of his men, Finn relented and again brought water to Diarmuid. But it was too late. Before Diarmuid could drink he breathed his last. Finn, wanting full revenge, cut off Diarmuid's head and sent it to Gráinne. Upon seeing it she collapsed and died. Her body was carried to a cave and the couple were buried there together, high up above the beautiful Gleniff Horseshoe Valley.

Both of these mountainous regions have a justifiable reputation for wild landscapes and more than a fair share of natural beauty. But they also bear the marks of early settlers who have left a cultural legacy of megalithic monuments, Celtic and early Christian heritage sites and ruined castles dating from more recent history.

The Fermanagh–Sligo–Cavan area

Home to the natural wonder that is the Marble Arch Caves Global Geopark, the mountainous upland and the gentle rolling lowland of counties Fermanagh and Cavan break into Co. Sligo and Co. Leitrim. Although not part of the Geopark Co. Sligo and Co. Leitrim are nevertheless geologically very rich. A geopark is an area recognised by UNESCO as having internationally significant geological heritage along with a policy for the sustainable use of that heritage for the benefit of local communities.

The Geopark, of Cavan and Fermanagh, and its world-famous Marble Arch Caves, taken together with other features such as the distinctive flat-topped Benbulben and rugged Ox Mountains in Co. Sligo and the soft hills of Cavan, means that the Fermanagh-Sligo-Cavan area can lay claim to some of the finest natural landscapes in Ireland.

In Fermanagh, dramatic cliffs, jagged rocky outcrops and upland blanket bog dominate in the north and west, while

The fantastic subterranean grottos with grooved surfaces and hanging stalactites at Marble Arch Caves in Co. Fermanagh are due to rainwater's ability to dissolve limestone

MYTHOLOGY AND GEOLOGY

Benaughlin, on the flanks of Cuilcagh Mountain

The speaking horse of Benaughlin

On the eastern slopes of Cuilcagh Mountain, the limestone has given rise to a distinctive rounded hill called Benaughlin, which comes from Binn Eachlabhra, or the 'peak of the speaking horse'. The horse in question is supposed to be a white horse (An Chopail Bán) and can be seen on the last Sunday of July every year when it talks to the local people. The horse belongs to the king of the Sídhe called Donn Binn. The king can be seen travelling around this part of Fermanagh on the horse every May eve at the start of the festival of Bealtaine when bonfires would be lit to welcome the coming of summer.

The cliffs bordering Glencar Lake in counties Leitrim and Sligo are formed of the same hard limestone as Benbulben

the landscape to the south, extending into Cavan, provides rolling drumlins and flooded hollows that exhibit some of the finest examples of landscapes created by glaciers in the world. A drumlin is a small rounded hill, the result of deposits left behind by ice sheets as they retreated from the region during the last Ice Age some 13,000 years ago (see page 31).

Water features prominently in the landscape of Fermanagh and Cavan. Co. Cavan claims a lake for every day of the year, and Co. Fermanagh is dominated by Upper Lough Erne and Lower Lough Erne, with the town of Enniskillen nestling on an island between the two expanses of water.

Cuilcagh Mountain and the Marlbank area provide further spectacular scenery.

At 665 m, Cuilcagh is the highest point and sits on the Cavan–Fermanagh border, its distinctive table-top profile forming the focus of an area rich in geology, archaeology, folklore, flora and fauna. Cuilcagh is topped by hard sandstone, exposed in places as impressive cliffs sweeping down to the lower sandstone and shale slopes.

The rocks throughout this region are mostly limestones, formed about 330 million years ago in a coral-filled tropical sea when Ireland was located on the equator. Many of the limestones here are rich in fossils, and because limestone dissolves in rainwater many complex underground cave systems have formed, including the amazing Marble Arch show caves (see page 20).

In Co. Sligo, Benbulben is one of Ireland's most recognisable mountains. Like Cuilcagh it too has a table-top profile but here is formed out of hard limestone. Benbulben is described famously in the poetry of William Butler Yeats, who today lies buried under its shadow at Drumcliff. To the east of Benbulben the same limestone forms the spectacular cliffs on the north side of Glencar, Co. Sligo.

Extending from the west in a narrow arc to the south and east of Sligo are the Ox Mountains. These are composed of a thin band of metamorphic rocks, which, at around 1,000 million years old, are among the oldest in Ireland. In contrast to the flat-topped hills such as Benbulben, the Ox Mountains present a much more rugged appearance, with a series of marked peaks visible on the skyline.

Carlingford Lough, flanked by the Mourne Mountains on the left and the Cooley Mountains to the right on the south side of the lough

Other important geological features can be found in the limestone plateau of the Burren in Co. Cavan, which is also now part of the Marble Arch Caves Global Geopark. Fine examples of glacial erratics (see page 33) can be found throughout this area, which also contains a predominance of Neolithic sites and settlements. The Irish word '*boíreann*', which gives the anglicised word 'burren', means 'a stony place' and has been applied to several places across Ireland.

The south Ulster drumlin belt

Recognised as an internationally important region for the study of drumlins, south Ulster's 'drumlin belt' comprising the rolling hills of the Down-Armagh-Monaghan-Cavan region, interspersed with lakes and wetlands, forms a unique physical and cultural landscape that is bounded to the south-east by three areas of high ground in the shape of the Ring of Gullion and the Mourne and Cooley Mountains.

Typical of the land and scenery in this region, the drumlin permeates the life, language and culture of south Ulster. For instance the Irish word for Monaghan, *Muineachán*, comes from '*Muine Cheain*', meaning the 'land of the little hills' and oftentimes these landforms are descriptively referred to as a 'basket of eggs' as that is what they look like when viewed from above. The poet Patrick Kavanagh wrote 'These are my Alps and this is my Matterhorn' of the hills of his native Inniskeen in south Monaghan.

The sea's flooding of areas where the drumlins reach the coast shows off the shape of drumlins particularly well. One of the best places to see this is

MYTHOLOGY AND GEOLOGY

The Ring of Gullion, Co. Armagh, is steeped in folklore – it was formed by magma seeping into a circular crack in the Earth's surface called a ring dyke

Culann's Hound

Slieve Gullion, in the south of Co. Armagh, is the setting for a story about one of the great Irish mythological heroes – Cúchulainn. Originally named Setanta, he was the son of the god Lugh and at the age of seven, as was the custom, he was sent to be fostered at Emain Macha by King Conchobhar. One evening the king and his entourage were to attend a feast hosted by his blacksmith Culann at his home on the slopes of Slieve Gullion. Setanta was finishing off a game of hurley and promised he would travel on his own as soon as it ended. When the entourage arrived at Slieve Gullion and as night fell, Culann set free his fearsome guard dog to patrol the boundary of his property. Setanta, unaware of the danger, and seeing the gates locked, climbed up over the wall to gain access. Culann's hound attacked out of the darkness but was no match for Setanta, who, armed with his hurley stick and *sliotar*, soon killed the hound. Culann was angry and demanded compensation. Setanta offered to act as a replacement for the dead hound until Culann had found and trained a new dog. Culann accepted, and Setanta was known thereafter as Cúchulainn – or Culann's Hound.

Many of the islands found in Strangford Lough are in fact drumlins drowned by rising sea levels after the Ice Age

The magnificent Mourne Mountains in Co. Down

At Kearney Point, Co. Down, sandstones and mudstones from the floor of the ancient Iapetus Ocean are bent and contorted from continental collisions that closed the oceans

Strangford Lough, Northern Ireland's only marine nature reserve, which is a drumlin lowland that has been flooded by sea level rise and now contains dozens of small islands.

The high ground of south Ulster – the Mourne Mountains, Slieve Gullion and the Cooley Mountains – is linked to the volcanic activity that took place in Co. Antrim around 60 million years ago. Slieve Gullion with its encircling Ring of Gullion and the Cooley Mountains are actually extinct volcanoes. Occurring slightly later than the eruptions on the Antrim Plateau, these mountains were once central volcanoes – a cone-shaped volcano with an opening, or vent, in the centre of its summit.

At 850 m, Slieve Donard in the Mournes is the highest mountain in Ulster. The Mournes are composed of pale-coloured granite, in contrast to the dark blue-grey of the Antrim basalts. Unlike the Ring of Gullion and Cooley the igneous activity in the Mournes happened below the surface and no lava ever erupted out onto the land. Instead the molten magma cooled slowly below the surface into granite.

While the sands that gathered near the shore of an ancient ocean were forming into the Donegal Mountains some 500 million years ago, further out in deeper waters lay thick layers of darker sands and muds. These rocks are now found in Down, Armagh, Monaghan and Cavan as a belt of grey sandstones and mudstones. As the ocean closed the pressures associated with the collisions of continents tilted these rocks from the horizontal to the vertical, as can be seen at Ballywalter or Kearney Point on the Co. Down coast.

MYTHOLOGY AND GEOLOGY

Slieve Gullion, Co. Armagh

The summit of Slieve Gullion

At its summit Slieve Gullion, or *Sliabh gCullin*, the 'mountain of the steep slope', there is a cairn, Calliagh Berra's House, and a lake, Calliagh Berra's Lake, which is reputed to be bottomless. Cailleach Beara was a sort of witch. It is said she once enticed the mighty Finn McCool into the house on the summit. From there she took him deep into the earth and into the roots of this ancient volcano. When he emerged, he had become an emaciated old man and it took him many years before he managed to regain his strength fully.

MYTHOLOGY AND GEOLOGY

Lough Neagh, the latest in the succession of lakes that have existed on Antrim's basalt over geological time

The lost towers of Lough Neagh

Lough Neagh is only the latest in a succession of lakes that have existed on top of the Antrim basalt for the last 25 million years. Science may have one explanation for its origin, but tradition has others … One story tells of an ancient kingdom that had deep within it a magical spring of bright, fresh water. But the people of this kingdom turned greedy and began to rob and cheat their neighbours. At first the spring did nothing but eventually it rose up in outrage, drowning the kingdom and everyone in it, leaving behind an enormous lake. It is said that the lost towers of this ancient kingdom can still be seen far beneath the waves of Lough Neagh.

Of course, no story of Lough Neagh can be told without mentioning Finn McCool. According to legend it is Finn who is responsible for creating the lough. It seems that he was having a quarrel with his enemy Fingal who lived across the sea. In his anger, Finn is reputed to have ripped up a huge sod of earth and tossed it out over the sea towards Fingal. The sod fell short of its target, instead dropping into the middle of the Irish Sea to form the Isle of Man while the enormous hole left behind soon filled with water to form Lough Neagh.

Now underlying most of the undulating countryside that typifies Co. Down and Co. Armagh, these rocks are an important source of crushed rock or aggregate in the local construction industry.

The Lough Neagh Basin and river valleys

After the volcanic turbulence that formed the Antrim Plateau, the region became quieter. But as a result of the massive weight of lavas that had erupted over the area, the Earth's surface sagged. It formed a saucer-like depression, now called the Lough Neagh Basin, which of course is today occupied by the largest area of fresh water in Britain and Ireland.

The higher ground around the basin has been eroded away and now forms thick deposits of clay and sandstones known

The Lough Neagh Basin was formed by sagging of the Earth's crust after the volcanic eruptions that built the Antrim Plateau and is now occupied by the largest area of fresh water in Britain and Ireland

MYTHOLOGY AND GEOLOGY

The Shannon Pot, source of the River Shannon

The Shannon Pot

The most spectacular example of a spring in Ireland must be the Shannon Pot in west Cavan, situated in the heart of the UNESCO-endorsed Marble Arch Caves Global Geopark. The Shannon Pot is a dramatic feature some 16 m in diameter and marking the source of the longest river in Ireland. The waters here were sacred and it was forbidden to eat the fruits of the hazel trees that encircled the water as they had the power to give foresight and all knowledge. But the grand-daughter of Manannan Mac Lír, the god of the Sea, greatly desired this power and knowledge and so picked one of the hazel nuts. As she bit into the nut, the waters sprang up and overwhelmed her and as they drained away they carved out a river that flowed far to the south. That river continues to flow today and carries the name of the unfortunate girl – Sionnan, or Shannon.

The source of the River Bann is in the Mourne Mountains

as the Lough Neagh Clays. At around 25 million years old these are the youngest rocks – clay is actually a rock – in Ireland and are important because they contain huge reserves of the brown coal, lignite. These coal deposits formed from the remains of dense woodland around the lake during this period. The tree species growing included giant sequoia and redwoods. Fossil leaves and bark from these great trees are commonly found in the lignite.

There has been much interest in these rocks and development of the lignite reserves is a controversial topic. It will probably only be finally resolved by innovative technology solutions that do not require large-scale opencast mining methods for extracting the coal.

Six major and various minor rivers flow into Lough Neagh, including Northern

Ireland's longest river, the Bann. The Upper Bann rises in the Mourne Mountains, Co. Down, and flows into the lough at its southern end. The Lower Bann drains the lough from its north end at Toome in Co. Antrim to the sea at Barmouth in Co. Londonderry. Collectively the rivers flowing into Lough Neagh drain more than a third of Northern Ireland's landscape, plus part of Co. Monaghan in the Republic of Ireland.

While the waterways of Lough Neagh, Lough Erne and the River Bann enhance the low-lying regions of the northern landscape, an abundance of attractive river valleys reinforces the scenic value of the higher ground. The Ice Age entering the scene in Northern Ireland (see page 31) heavily influenced these landscape features. The great ice sheets moved over Ireland in a slow but sure way. As rivers of ice, or glaciers, flowed down valleys

Glenoe, Co. Antrim

they cut deeply into their floors and sides, widening them into a u-shaped profile. The advancing and retreating glaciers abraded and plucked at the valleys and when they finally melted the rivers reclaimed these valleys, which were now much deeper and wider than before.

The nine Glens of Antrim – the word glen comes from the Irish word for valley, *gleann* – are among the most well-known and picturesque, and the Glenelly Valley in Co. Tyrone is regarded as one of the most idyllic. In the west, the Foyle Valley as a whole is drained by the Foyle, Mourne, Strule, Glenmornan and Derg rivers and consists of a widespread collection of landforms all linked by the marks of the Ice Age.

Elsewhere, the very broad and flat Lagan Valley hosts the River Lagan, which flows in a winding, narrow channel into the sea at hill-ringed Belfast Lough. The Lagan's riverbank scenery, meadows, woods and farmland are part of the Irish pastoral idyll, and within this landscape there is a rich variety of man-made features testifying to some 9,000 years of human settlement.

Malin Head, Co. Donegal, the most northerly point on the Irish mainland

IRELAND'S WORLD TOUR

The spectacular landscape of the northern part of Ireland is the result of a series of incredible events such as long periods of volcanic activity, earthquakes, ocean openings and closings and continent collisions – geological forces stretching back millions of years. Understanding these forces and recognising the timescale involved in the formation of Ireland's landmass is one of the challenges of fully appreciating the scenery surrounding us today (see page 17, Time on a vast scale).

The Earth is about 4.5 billion years old (4,500 million). The oldest rocks so far discovered are over four billion years old (4,000,000,000), and are found in northern Canada. The oldest rocks in Ireland are about 1.8 billion years old. One place you can see them is on the island of Inishtrahull, off Malin Head in Co. Donegal. Erosion over long periods of time has destroyed much of the geological evidence concerning the earliest stages of the Earth, but it is still possible to piece together the evidence of the geological history of Ireland and its journey across the world from about 600 million years ago.

Ireland's current position on the globe is about six degrees west of the Greenwich Meridian, the imaginary line that runs from the North Pole to the South Pole through Greenwich in London, and around 54 degrees north of the equator, which runs around the centre of the Earth. But we have travelled far to get here. This is because the Earth's continents are constantly on the move.

Large sections – called plates – of the Earth's outermost layer are moving slowly but constantly across the planet's surface like pieces of a giant jigsaw. The plates are moving away from each other, towards each other or simply moving past each other, slowly, a few centimetres per year, steadily changing the location of Earth's continents and oceans (see page 14, How the Earth moves – plate tectonics).

When geologists plot positions for roughly the last 500 million years of Earth history they can show that for 450 million of those years the part of the Earth's crust we now know as Ireland moved steadily northwards and eastwards. It started on the opposite side of the globe far from its present location, somewhere in the Pacific, east of Australia in the southern hemisphere. It crossed the equator about 350 million years ago and carried on drifting northwards to reach its present position.

> **" Rocks are records of events that took place at the time they formed. They are books. They have a different vocabulary, a different alphabet, but you learn how to read them. "**
>
> **John McPhee**
> **American Pulitzer Prize-winning author**

The island of Inishtrahull, nearly 10 km off the north Donegal coast, consists of 1,800-million-year-old rocks, the oldest found anywhere in Ireland

DID YOU KNOW?

Oceans, in particular an ancient one called the Iapetus Ocean, played a big part in Ireland's journey across the globe

Geologists can tell from fossils that the closure of the Iapetus Ocean brought together the two parts of Ireland. Fossils from animals that once lived on either side of this ancient sea show sufficient differences to be recognised as two separate populations. The fossils in rocks of the age of the Iapetus Ocean from the northern half of Ireland are similar to those collected from Newfoundland in Canada. Yet fossils from areas such as Wexford in southern Ireland show links with the English Lake District, Wales and certain Baltic countries. Why? It is thought the Iapetus was too wide for the animals to cross and allow the populations to mix, thus the two parts of Ireland must once have been thousands of kilometres apart. Thus only when the ocean had shrunk enough, bringing the two parts of Ireland together, could the species mix and this is reflected in the rock record of later periods.

DID YOU KNOW?

Ama Dablam, Nepal in the Himalayas

At their maximum extent the Caledonides were on a par with the present-day Himalayan mountain chain, which of course contains the highest mountain on Earth, Mount Everest. You can still see the remains of these massive mountains in Donegal, the Sperrins, in north-east Antrim between Murlough Bay and Torr Head, and across the Irish Sea in the Highlands of Scotland and further afield in Norway and the Appalachians of the USA. The Caledonides are of worldwide importance to developing key concepts in mountain range formation. Understanding the evolution of this mountain range has broadened understanding of geological time and supported theories about continental change. This process is ongoing today as the Tibetan plateau is still rising at the rate of a few centimetres per year as India continues to push northwards into Asia.

DID YOU KNOW?

How the Earth moves – plate tectonics

The Earth's outermost layer, or crust, is fragmented into numerous pieces called plates. These plates carry the continents and oceans and are moving slowly but constantly across the planet's surface. The theory of how the plates move is called plate tectonics. Plates are either moving away from each other, towards each other or sliding past each other. In the process they slowly but surely allow our continents and oceans to drift across the surface of the Earth.

San Andreas – across the dividing line

Elkhorn Hills, Carrizo Plain, California, and a view along the famous San Andreas Fault

The sharp distinction between the Elkhorn Hills and the Carrizo Plain in the image is the result of plate movements. The dividing line is probably the most famous earthquake zone anywhere on Earth. At the San Andreas Fault a plate consisting mostly of Pacific Ocean crust is moving past the North American plate

at a rate of about 1 cm per year. As the two parts of the crust move past each other, friction causes them to become jammed. Pressure builds up and eventually the plates overcome the friction and, in a series of jolts or shudders, move another short distance. These are the sudden movements that generate the earthquake waves so catastrophic to built-up areas. They devastated San Francisco in the Great Earthquake of 1906.

Take a look below Earth's surface

At Þingvellír in southern Iceland you can clearly see the rift between two separating plates. Þingvellír sits on the rifting boundary between the European and North American plates, a rift that continues down the middle of the Atlantic Ocean. One side of this deep crack or fissure is moving slowly east towards Europe. The other is moving west towards North America, widening the Atlantic Ocean by a few centimetres a year

The outer layer of the planet, the crust, is relatively thin. Under the continents it is about 40 km thick, but it is much less, only about 10 km thick, under the oceans. Directly under the crust is a zone called the mantle, going down to almost 3,000 km from the surface. Below this is the central zone of the Earth, the core. The core consists mostly of iron and it is about 7,000 km in diameter and very hot – around 6,000°C.

Although the mantle is solid, it can flow very slowly like thick porridge. As the core heats the lower parts of the mantle it becomes lighter and begin to rise, forming an ascending current of warmed material. This rising current comes to the surface and is deflected sideways by the cooler, brittle crust. In moving sideward the mantle exerts enough force on the base of the crust to split it and pull it apart. The split is filled by volcanic eruptions.

When this process happens on the sea floor it is called sea-floor spreading and the ocean gradually gets wider as two plate edges are pushed further apart. This process is like a conveyor belt with new ocean crust continually being created at the ridge and being pushed away at the rate of a few centimetres a year. The volcanic activity pushes the ocean floor up into a high ridge, called the mid-ocean ridge, and these mid-ocean mountain ranges are a feature of all the deep ocean basins on the planet. Activity on the northern part of the Mid-Atlantic Ridge has been so intense over the last few million years that its top has broken through the surface of the ocean to form the volcanic island of Iceland. Geologists believe the high concentration of volcanic activity is because of a combination of Iceland's position on the Mid-Atlantic Ridge and a volcanic hotspot underneath the island. The ash cloud spewing from the Eyjafjallajökull volcano in 2010 was evidence that the process is continuing.

Colliding plates

Since the Earth is not expanding, to balance areas like the Atlantic, which are getting larger, there must be regions on the Earth's surface that are shrinking. One such area is the Pacific Ocean. This is because around the edges of the Pacific the plates are colliding. When plates collide the forces push one plate edge underneath the other, resulting in severe earthquakes. Whenever a plate carrying an ocean collides with a plate carrying a continent, it is always the ocean-carrying plate that is pushed below the continental plate. The frequent and often catastrophic earthquakes that occur in Japan for example, are because the ocean floor around the Japanese islands is being pushed underneath the continental crust of Asia to the west.

As the descending plate is pushed deeper into the interior of the Earth it becomes hotter and eventually melts. This liquid rock rises towards the surface like an oil droplet in water and these volumes of liquefied crust can form large volcanoes such as Mount Pinatubo in the Philippines. The long chains of volcanoes of the Andes in South America and the Cascades in the USA formed in this way.

The largest ever volcanic eruption in historical time was at Mount Tambora, Indonesia, in 1815. The eruption killed 100,000 people, unleashed deadly tsunamis and ejected so much assorted ash and grit into the atmosphere that a global cooling occurred and 1816 became known as 'the year without a summer'. It is not a well-known eruption because there was no modern media to report it.

The ash cloud produced by the eruption of Mount St Helens in Washington State, USA in 1980. The eruption killed more than 60 people, flattened millions of trees and covered much of the western states of the USA in a thick blanket of grey ash

The line of volcanic cones at Lakagígar sits on the Mid-Atlantic Ridge – its eruption in 1783 was the largest outpouring of lava by volume in recorded history

Glendun, Co. Antrim, one of the nine glens adorning the Antrim Plateau

DID YOU KNOW?

Time on a vast scale

Geologists and astronomers are the two groups whose scientific discipline requires dealing with the vastness of time as represented by the age of the universe and the formation of the universe. For many people coming to geology for the first time, the extent of geological time is the aspect of the subject they find most difficult to deal with.

One minute to midnight

One of the early thinkers about the immensity of geological time was James Hutton, a scientist and philosopher working in Edinburgh in the second half of the eighteenth century. His famous remark: "We see no vestige of a beginning, no prospect of an end" recognised that very many years were needed to account for the features that made up the landscape

The digital clock shows the approximate time of arrival of Homo sapiens on Earth, if the full extent of geological time is represented by a single 24-hour day

he was familiar with in Scotland. This was linked to his realisation that the processes operating in the landscape today, the weathering and erosion of the rocks on the Earth's surface, were the same as those that had operated throughout geological time. Modern estimates put the age of the solar system, of which Earth is a part, at 4,600 million years (4.6 billion years). The oldest rocks preserved on the planet's surface are just over four billion years old.

If we compare the full extent of geological time to a 24-hour day, then if the Earth formed at 00.00 hours, in orbit around the newly formed sun, then the first living cells did not appear until around 07.00 hours, some 3,600 million years ago. The so-called 'explosion of life' in Cambrian times around 500 million years ago, when creatures such as trilobites inhabited the ocean floors, would have taken place at about 21.20 hours on our clock. Life on land started sometime after 22.00 hours. The development of hominid forms, leading eventually to Homo sapiens, began about one minute to midnight.

Measurement of geological time

Time is so important to geology it is worth taking a look at the techniques used by geologists to unravel its complexities and to provide a framework for measurement.

Relative time

Initially geologists measured time in a relative way only. That is, they could describe a rock only as being older or younger than another rock, without attempting to calculate its age in years. This could be done because in any sequence of sedimentary rocks, for example in a quarry face, the oldest rock would be at the bottom, the youngest would be at the top. Geologists call this the Law of Superposition. As well as using this technique it was realised that rocks from different localities which contained similar fossils were formed at the same time, because there is the same progression of fossil life forms from older to younger beds in all parts of the world. This is the Law of Faunal Succession. Using these principles on a world-wide scale from the mid-nineteenth century onwards what's called a geological or stratigraphical column was developed that placed the principal periods of Earth history in order and showing the gradual evolution of life as indicated by the fossil remains in the rocks.

Absolute time

After the establishment of the stratigraphical column as a relative time scale, efforts were then made from the early twentieth century onwards to develop an absolute time scale, where

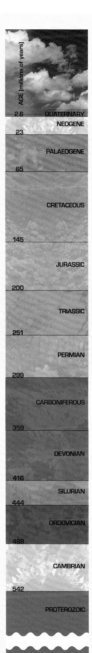

AGE (millions of years)	
2.6	QUATERNARY
23	NEOGENE
65	PALAEOGENE
145	CRETACEOUS
200	JURASSIC
251	TRIASSIC
299	PERMIAN
359	CARBONIFEROUS
416	DEVONIAN
444	SILURIAN
488	ORDOVICIAN
542	CAMBRIAN
4500	PROTEROZOIC

The stratigraphical column showing the main sub-divisions and periods of geological time, as used by geologists

the age of the rocks could be calculated in actual numbers of years.

The breakthrough in measuring absolute time came with the discovery of radioactivity, the ability of certain elements such as uranium to emit energy in the form of radiation and by doing so change their composition. In the case of uranium it changes to lead. The rate at which this energy is emitted is constant for that element and so by measuring the amount of uranium and lead present in a mineral, the length of time the process has been going on can be calculated. The older the rock, the greater the amount of lead that will have been formed from the original uranium. This is called radiometric dating and by calculating the ages of many samples from all over the world it has been possible to put ages to the periods of the stratigraphical column and show the rocks not only in sequence, but also within a precisely timed framework.

Two Irelands an ocean apart

Ireland's journey is bound up with the birth, life and death of an expanse of water called the Iapetus Ocean. Ireland's story begins about 700 million years ago when all of the Earth's continents had drifted together, forming a 'supercontinent' called Rodinia.

The main components of the supercontinent were two landmasses: Laurentia and Gondwana. Laurentia consisted of what we would now recognise as the oldest parts of North America, together with parts of Europe and Russia, while Gondwana comprised the continents found now in the southern hemisphere South America, Africa, Australia and Antarctica.

Sometime around 610 million years ago, rifting within this supercontinent led to the birth of a new ocean. The new ocean widened as the two parts of the former Rodinia moved away from each other. The northern portions of what would become Ireland were part of Laurentia while the southern portions were in

The globe shows distribution of the Earth's continents 600 million years ago

Torr Head, Co. Antrim, looking across the Sea of Moyle to Kintyre in Scotland, both part of the great Caledonian Mountain range

Gondwana and as the ocean widened they drifted further and further apart. As it was a sort of pre-Atlantic Ocean it was given the name Iapetus, who in Greek mythology was the father of Atlas after whom the Atlantic is named.

But after about 100 million years the Iapetus Ocean had reached its maximum width and started to close again as movements in the Earth's mantle caused the continents on either side of the Iapetus to drift towards each other. As it shrank, its ocean floor became squeezed and compressed as tectonic forces pushed the vast continents on either side of it towards each other as if in the jaws of a gigantic vice. Fragments of Gondwana began to break off and move into collision with Laurentia. Over a period of 50 million years (from

470–420 million years ago) a series of these collisions not only led to the total destruction of the Iapetus Ocean but also to the formation of a major new chain of mountains known to geologists as the Caledonian Mountains. These mountains were similar in scope to the present-day Himalayas (also formed by continental collision, in this case the collision of India with Asia). They extended continuously from what we know today as northern Norway, across Scotland and Ireland and on unbroken into Newfoundland, eastern Canada and along the eastern seaboard of the USA. Remember, this was millions of years before the present day Atlantic existed. Geologists know from some of the types of minerals present in the rocks of these ancient mountains that they were probably higher in places than today's Himalayas.

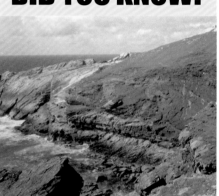
The formation of the Caledonides had a great influence on the geology of Ireland. Much of the scenery in the more rugged areas of Donegal owes its character to this major event in Ireland's geological history. The Donegal Highlands, along with the rocks of the Sperrin Mountains, are remnants of the Caledonian Mountains, and contain, in fact, the last traces of the Iapetus Ocean.

The massively increased temperatures and pressures involved in mountain building alter the nature of rocks. Such forces changed the sandstones, limestones and mudstones (sedimentary rocks) that originally formed on the floor of the Iapetus Ocean into quartzites,

Sandstones on the Co. Down coast bent and folded by the massive forces involved in the closing of the Iapetus Ocean

marbles and schists, which are types of metamorphic rock (see page 94). Bent and warped like plasticine, tightly folded sandstones placed under this plate tectonic strain and heat can be seen near Millisle, Co. Down. The cliffs at

Slieve League in south Donegal are also excellent illustrations of the metamorphic rocks from these times.

Another predominant rock type in the north of Ireland is granite, and much of

Streedagh Point, Co. Sligo, is a marine graveyard of corals and shellfish from more than 300 million years ago

An important geological heritage site at Streedagh Point on the Sligo coast contains a sequence of fossil-rich limestone rocks. It provides the best evidence we have that 330 million years ago Ireland was submerged under a tropical sea teeming with corals, shellfish and sea lilies. One site is known as Serpent Rock, in reference to the fossils' similarity in appearance to snakes. Both the Streedagh Point and Serpent Rock sites, essentially a large marine graveyard, are very important and you should never hammer the rocks or take away the fossils.

The cliffs at Slieve League, Co. Donegal, were formed out of metamorphic rocks like quartzite and marble as the sandstones and limestones on the floor of the Iapetus Ocean were crushed and heated during the formation of the Caledonian Mountains

this owes its existence to the closure of Iapetus Ocean and the mountain-building phase that produced the Caledonian Mountains. The intense tectonic forces involved in the closing of the ocean pushed the oceanic crust back into the Earth's mantle and here it partially melted to create molten rock, which then moved upwards towards the surface before cooling and hardening as granite. These type of rock formations are found all over central and north Donegal, for example near An Clochán Liath (Dungloe) and the rugged coastline of the Fanad Peninsula in north Donegal.

Trabeg Bay, Fanad, Co. Donegal. Here the jointing of the Fanad granite, the result of shrinkage as it cooled, is clearly exposed

DID YOU KNOW?

Marble Arch Caves, Co. Fermanagh

Limestone is the most common rock type over the whole of Ireland and the dominant rock in the Fermanagh lakelands and in north Co. Sligo. Formed some 330 million years ago in the Carboniferous Period, it is limestone that gives this part of Ireland its special character. The rock has some unusual properties from a geological perspective. In particular, ordinary rainwater can dissolve it. This is because limestone is mostly made of calcium carbonate (the mineral calcite) and is alkaline, whereas rainwater is naturally slightly acidic. So, over time, rainwater can eat away at the limestone, slowly dissolving its way into the rock. This geological process, taking place over many thousands of years, results in unusual surface and subsurface features ranging from sinkholes, disappearing streams and springs, to complex underground drainage systems and caves. In time, vast underground chambers or caves can open up, such as we see at the celebrated Marble Arch Caves Global Geopark. After the action of water opens up the cave the creation of some of the other features begins. Water, containing dissolved limestone (calcite), drips or runs from the cave roof. As each drop of water falls, a tiny amount of calcite gets left behind. Over time these accumulate into hanging pillars called stalactites, Similarly, when a drop reaches the cave floor and evaporates, some calcite is left behind, eventually accumulating into a stalagmite. These features often join together as a pillar. Taken together, all these limestone features form what geologists call a karst landscape. The area around the Marble Arch caves and the Marlbank of south-west Fermanagh and the adjacent Burren of west Cavan are typical karst landscapes.

Two become one

The closure of the Iapetus Ocean and the resulting prolonged mountain-building phase was to bring together the two parts of Ireland and put in place the framework for the rest of the geological structure of the island.

With the disappearance of Iapetus and the formation of the vast Caledonian Mountain chain, the scene was set for a complete change of geological environment for Ireland. By around 400 million years ago, in what is known as Devonian times (416–359 million years ago), the closure of the Iapetus Ocean had created a new and larger continent. Ireland was located on its south-eastern margins, in tropical latitudes, just south of the equator with the vast Caledonian Mountain chain to the north-west.

The massive mountain chain nearby severely limited the amount of rainfall over the area of Ireland and produced

The globe shows the distribution of the continents after the closure of Iapetus Ocean around 420 million years ago

hot desert conditions – in effect a rain shadow similar to areas such as Death Valley in California, which is deprived of rain by the close-by Sierra Nevada mountain range.

At this stage of the evolution of life on Earth land plants were not well

Conglomerates or 'pudding stone' rock at Cushendun, Co. Antrim, are the result of the very fast weathering of the massive Caledonian Mountain chain

The slopes of the flat-topped Benbulben, Co. Sligo, are covered by piles of loose rocks called screes, formed by weathered blocks falling from the upper slopes

developed. The Caledonian Mountains had little protective vegetation cover and so were easily weathered and eroded. This meant that huge thicknesses of desert sediments, composed mostly of sandstones and their coarser variation, conglomerates, formed at their edges. Today these are exposed in places such as the coastal caves around Cushendun in Co. Antrim.

Rocks formed in hot desert conditions are typically reddish brown, due to the iron content of the rock oxidising or rusting in the atmosphere. Collectively these rocks are often referred to as Old Red Sandstone. In the north of Ireland these are also found, for example, in the Clogher Valley, Co. Tyrone, and into east Fermanagh and at Fanad in Co. Donegal.

The inhospitable, arid environment changed as Ireland drifted northwards. Sea gradually advanced from the south-east and over a time span of about 30 million years it encroached northwards, eventually reaching its most northerly extent in the Fermanagh and south Donegal area about 330 million years ago. Ireland had now reached the equator on its northward journey. This period of time is marked by the development of the world's first great rain forests. Vast tree ferns dominated and there were high growth rates of vegetation. Giant insects and arthropods (for example, scorpions) inhabited these forests, while elsewhere giant amphibians colonised the land. Thick coal beds formed as the vegetation of the great forests died, decomposed,

became buried and compressed. The spectacular fossil corals found in limestone at Streedagh Point in Co. Sligo tell some of the story of the warm tropical environment that prevailed in what geologists call the Carboniferous (360–299 million years ago), around 330 million years ago.

In Ireland, the advancing sea formed deposits of sandstones from sand that settled onto the floor of the Carboniferous sea. These were replaced by limestones as the water deepened. Carboniferous limestone is the most commonly found bedrock in Ireland and in the north it lies under much of Fermanagh, Leitrim and Sligo, extending around a large part of Donegal Bay.

White Park Bay, Co. Antrim, bounded by cliffs of chalk and basalt

DID YOU KNOW?

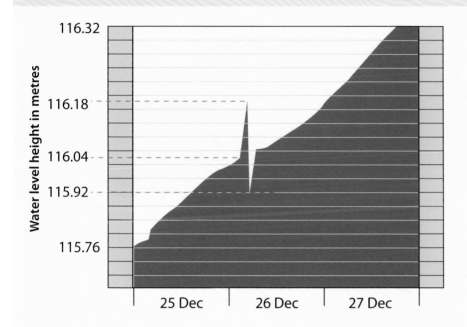

The diagram shows changes in well water level at Killyglen, Co. Antrim, as the shock waves from the 26 December earthquake in 2004 passed through the Earth's interior, causing a rise and fall of nearly 30 cm

The movement of the Earth's tectonic plates relative to each other is responsible for most of the earthquakes and volcanic eruptions found at the surface. The main reason why Northern Ireland has relatively few earthquakes and no active volcanoes is because it is located well away from any of the boundaries between these tectonic plates. Although earthquakes strong enough to be felt by the population in Ireland are relatively rare, the effects do not go unnoticed. When a major earthquake happens it produces shock waves that radiate out in all directions from the focus of the earthquake. These waves are like the noise produced when a bell is struck by its clapper. In effect the whole Earth rings like a bell after a major earthquake and these vibrations can be detected in various ways.

After the earthquake that caused the disastrous Indian Ocean tsunami in December 2004, water levels in wells in Ireland rose and fell significantly as the shock waves passed through this part of the Earth's outermost layer, or crust. This happened within minutes of the earthquake even though it took place thousands of kilometres away on the other side of the world. In one well in Co. Antrim the water level rose and fell over a range of about 30 cm as the shock waves travelled through the crust. The speed of the earthquake waves varies, but they commonly range from 2–10 km per second.

Relocation north of the equator

In the roughly 300 million years since Rodinia had started to break up with the formation of the Iapetus Ocean, the various fragments of the supercontinent had been dispersed around the globe by the internal forces driving plate tectonics. But now, towards the end of Carboniferous times, those continents were coming back together to form another supercontinent, this one known as Pangea, Greek for all-land.

This pattern of supercontinent formation followed by its break up, followed by the formation of yet another supercontinent, seems to have occurred since the earliest geological times on Earth.

One of the consequences of the formation of Pangea was a global drop in sea levels by perhaps as much as 100 m. These major changes in global sea-levels are linked to the levels of plate tectonic activity. When continents are widely dispersed there is a great deal

The globe shows the distribution of continents during Pangea times around 350 million years ago

of volcanic activity on the mid-ocean ridges and they expand with the heat, causing sea level to rise (see page 14). Correspondingly when the continents come together to form a supercontinent such as Pangea, volcanic activity is low, the ridges are cool and have a lower volume and so sea level drops.

At this stage Ireland was positioned north of the equator, close to the latitudes of the present-day Sahara Desert. Now (around 300 million years ago), as in the earlier Devonian times, Ireland was deep within a continental area and hot desert conditions had again taken hold. This change of geological environment was the beginning of Permian times in Earth history and marked the beginning of nearly 100 million years when Ireland's climatic conditions were mostly hot desert, except for some periods when parts of the area were invaded by shallow seas.

The 'Great Dying', the largest extinction of life on Earth, marked the end of the Permian Period 251 million years ago and the beginning of Triassic times on the geological timescale. Scientists estimate that up to 90% of all species died out both on land and in the oceans at this time. Theories about its causes include massive volcanic eruptions and resulting severe climate changes.

The Triassic formed the second part of Ireland's arid stay north of the equator. During this time Ireland was still part of Pangea and still in a similar position to the Sahara Desert today. The baking dry climate and low-lying plains were crossed by rivers carrying large amounts of sand. The sand was deposited on the

Desert sandstones formed in Triassic times still lie at Scrabo quarries, Newtownards, Co. Down

DID YOU KNOW?

Ripple marks preserved in the sandstone at Scrabo in Co. Down show that the lakes and rivers that existed here some 250 million years ago were often shallow, while fossilised mud cracks also found in the same rocks tells us that the rivers and lakes periodically dried up. The environment in Northern Ireland then was very similar to present-day Death Valley in California. The mud cracks in each area, 250 million years apart, are remarkably similar. So by observing how these features form today in California, geologists can work out how the very same features must have formed in Ireland 250 million years ago. The 'present is the key to the past' is one of the fundamental principles of geology.

Mud cracks formed under modern desert conditions

Fossil mud cracks from the ancient deserts of Scrabo

plains and then blown into dunes by the wind.

The layers of sandstone formed then can still be seen today in the old quarries on the side of Scrabo Hill, near Newtownards in Co. Down. Ripple marks preserved in the sandstone there show that the lakes and rivers that the sand was deposited from were often shallow, and the occurrence of mud cracks tells us that the rivers and lakes periodically dried up. The mud cracks in the present-day desert in Death Valley, California, are remarkably similar to those preserved in the 250-million-year-old sandstones in the Scrabo quarries.

Triassic times marked the start of the so-called Age of Reptiles and although a desert environment does not readily lend itself to the preservation of fossil remains, there has been one famous find in Scrabo of a reptile footprint. It is from a *Cheirotherium*, a lizard-like creature that roamed the desert plains on the edge of Pangea about 240 million years ago.

Drowned in warm shallow seas

As the Triassic Period progressed, the desert landscapes of north-east Ireland gradually began to change as the sea encroached once more on the land. Arms of the open ocean to the north infiltrated into the region, only to become repeatedly cut off from the open waters, which caused them to evaporate. This happened many, many times and gave rise to the thick salt deposits that now feed the salt-mining industry around Carrickfergus, Co. Antrim.

The advances in the sea that produced the salt deposits in Triassic times continued and deepening water heralded a change to full open sea conditions that characterised the next period of the Earth's history, the

The Age of Reptiles in Ireland – a footprint impression of Cheirothyrium, a lizard-like creature that roamed the desert plains of north Down about 240 million years ago

Jurassic. It lasted for 54 million years until about 145 million years ago.

The beginning of the Jurassic coincided with the beginning of the break-up of Pangea, a process that would eventually lead to the continental distribution we are familiar with today. In Northern Ireland we can trace the

The globe shows distribution of continents around 60 million years ago as the North Atlantic was opening and the Antrim basalts were beginning to erupt

Jurassic in sediments deposited on the floor of a shallow sea in the form of mudstones and thin limestones that often contain abundant fossil ammonites, related to squids, shellfish similar to modern cockles and oysters and occasional marine reptile remains. A good example is a dark grey clay with thin limestone bands which occurs underneath the white chalk around the Antrim Coast.

During Jurassic times Pangea continued to split into two large landmasses – named Laurentia and Gondwana – and by early in the next geological time period, the Cretaceous, South America, Antarctica and Australia had separated from Africa. Cretaceous times in Earth history are named after *creta*, the Latin for chalk. Chalk is composed of billions of skeletons of micro-organisms known as coccoliths, which lived in this sea. Their skeletons, made of the mineral calcite, fell to the sea-bed after death and

DID YOU KNOW?

Portbraddan, White Park Bay, Co. Antrim

Geologists can often prove there are faults in the Earth's crust when different rock types that geologically should be separate from each other, are found close to each other. A good example is the Portbraddan Fault, which runs roughly east–west along the north Antrim coast. Generally in Antrim the dark basalt cliffs are always above the whitish chalk cliffs. This is because the basalts are younger and were erupted on the top of the original chalk land surface. The Portbraddan Fault brings the two rock types to the same level, with the basalt lowered to sea level on the north side of the fault. You can easily see this at the harbour at Ballintoy, where the port is exactly on the fault line. The basalt has moved down by at least the thickness of the chalk. Also at White Park Bay the fault line has left distinctive chalk sea stacks on one side, and an elephant-shaped basalt stack on the other. The same contrast exists at the far end of White Park Bay as the fault line cuts directly through the village of Portbraddan.

formed a thick deposit of white chalk or limestone over much of western Europe. By about 90 million years ago sea levels worldwide were as much as 200 m above present levels. In Ireland this resulted in the remaining land surfaces becoming drowned by a warm shallow sea in which the chalk was deposited.

Another mass extinction happened at the end of Cretaceous times, 65 million years ago. Its best known victims were the dinosaurs, but many other life forms were also wiped out. There is now substantial evidence that at least part of the cause was a collision between

Earth and a comet or asteroid in Central America, but as with the earlier Permian mass extinction, there may have been other factors involved.

Around the same time there was extensive volcanic activity as North America began separating from Europe and the widening Atlantic Ocean continued to extend northwards. The ramifications of this splitting of Europe from America were to dominate the geology of north-east Ireland for the next five million years and give us, as we shall see, one of our premier geological attractions, the Giant's Causeway.

The Giant's Causeway, Co. Antrim

The tops of the remarkably regular hexagonal columns of the Giant's Causeway

The columns of the middle causeway catch the last of the day's sun at the Giant's Causeway

FORCES THAT CHANGED OUR LANDSCAPE

Despite our tendency to consider Earth as static, it is actually a dynamic, ever-changing planet. Volcanic activity and earthquakes alter the landscape in a dramatic and often violent manner. Wind, water, and ice erode and shape the land. And, as we have seen, on a much longer timescale the movement of Earth's plates slowly reconfigures oceans and continents, builds mountains and wipes them out again over the eons. As it continues to cool, what was once a hot lava world has become a possibly unique, temperate planet, hospitable to life with over two thirds of its surface covered by water.

Over time, two major forces, or sets of events and processes, have been particularly influential in shaping the Earth, and therefore the landscape of the northern portion of Ireland. We have already discussed the first, the mountain building and other changes associated, over hundreds of millions of years, with global-level plate tectonics. The most arresting and eye-catching rock formation in the Irish landscape left behind as a consequence of these plate tectonic forces is undoubtedly the area of mostly hexagonal basalt columns at the famed UNESCO World Heritage Site, the Giant's Causeway.

> **"We learn geology the morning after the earthquake."**
>
> **Ralph Waldo Emerson**
> **American poet and essayist**
> **The Conduct of Life, 1860**

The second set of forces are the erosion and weathering processes, those operating at the present time and those that have operated, with stunning long-term effect, over tens of millions of years. Weathering is the mechanical and chemical hammer that breaks down and sculpts the rocks. Erosion transports the fragments away. The impact of ice in particular, involving several glaciations and de-glaciations within the last million years, has scoured and carved the Irish landscape, while water, wind, frost, chemical reactions and other forces have worn and eroded mountains, dumped the debris all around us and largely determined the shape or appearance of our landscape and the composition of its soils.

Volcanic eruptions fit for giants

The story of the Giant's Causeway begins approximately 60 million years ago at a point when Ireland was in the midst of a volcanic and tectonically active region.

As Europe and North America rifted apart, the Earth's crust under north-east Ireland became stretched and at depth large volumes of rock melted to form magma. This magma then rose to the surface where it was expelled through vast volcanic eruptions as lava. Lava is the term for magma after it erupts to the surface. Lava can have different compositions and when it cools it therefore gives rise to different types

A view of the Giant's Causeway at the east side of Port Noffer where the bright red laterite layer marks a prolonged break in the eruptions that formed the Causeway Basalts

Looking towards the headland known as Aird Snout across the 100-m-thick lava flow that forms the Causeway

of rock. In our case, the lava give rise to the rock called basalt and it is most famously found in the form of the mostly hexagonal, vertical columns found today at the remarkable attraction on the north Antrim coast. This very special and relatively rare geological phenomenon, surrounded by many enduring myths and legends, provided a major landscape-shaping event for the northern part of Ireland, which is enjoyed today by over half a million visitors annually.

Just before the eruptions started, Antrim had been a low undulating chalk landscape covered by patches of vegetation. The first flows of the Antrim basalts erupted onto this surface. The split, or rift, in the Earth's crust that was separating North America from Europe extended north along western Scotland and further northwards still along eastern

Greenland (remember the Atlantic did not exist yet). So lava of the same type and age as we find in north-east Ireland is also found on Greenland and large areas of western Scotland, including the Isles of Skye and Mull. However, as the continents drifted apart, the volcanic activity moved away from Ireland.

Today the Atlantic is still widening and the volcanic activity is now concentrated along a ridge that runs north–south down the middle of the Atlantic Ocean. This mid-Atlantic Ridge marks the line where new oceanic crust continues to form as Europe and North America continue to move apart. The volcanic activity appears above sea level at Iceland and indeed the volcanic landscape of our northern neighbour gives us a good idea of how Antrim would have looked 60 million years ago.

The familiar scenery of the Antrim Coast was formed by the burying of the chalk surface under successive lava flows, building up the Antrim Plateau like the layers on a giant multiple sandwich. Volcanic activity caused the lava to erupt through long cracks or fissures in the Earth's crust. In some places the eruptions were very violent, with huge blocks of lava and ash blown out of the volcanic vents. The eruption at Eyjafjallajökull in Iceland in 2010 that led to the unprecedented disruption to air travel is an example of the type of eruption that happened in Antrim.

But the formation of the Antrim Plateau was not the result of a single volcanic eruption that proceeded from beginning to end. There appears to have been a slowdown of the activity that produced the first lavas followed by a period of dormancy when volcanic activity almost entirely ceased. During this time a warm, wet climate that produced an abundance of plants and trees including hazel, oak and various conifers, deeply weathered the lava surface across north-east Ireland. When basalt lava is weathered under these conditions its very high iron content forms a bright red soil the colour of rust that forms on iron metal exposed to the atmosphere. This weathered layer, called laterite, can still be seen in many places in Northern Ireland, particularly at the 'Giant's Eyes' at the Giant's Causeway, and over the years has been mined as a source of iron and aluminium ores.

The dormant period ended when another set of lavas were erupted. These were destined to become one of Ireland's most popular visitor attractions. The iconic

The western edge of the plateau basalts can be seen at Binevenagh, near Limavady, Co. Londonderry

Carrick-a-Rede's volcanic landscape and famous rope-bridge

Carrick-a-Rede is the largest example of the several volcanic vents you can find along the north Antrim coast, including at the nearby Kenbane Head. A volcanic vent is an opening in the Earth's crust through which lava and rock fragments erupt. Volcanic ash, including some larger blocks referred to as 'volcanic bombs' are thrown up into the air by the force of the eruption before falling back down to Earth. The ash material in the volcanic vent is more easily eroded than the surrounding rock, in this case cliffs of basalt and chalk. Over time the sea has cut a narrow passage through this softer rock, separating Carrick-a-Rede Island from the mainland. The now famous rope-bridge was constructed to allow salmon fishermen to cross over the traces of this ancient volcanic activity to their nets and cottages on the island.

DID YOU KNOW?

Slemish, Co. Antrim

The north-east of Ireland is a volcanic landscape composed of lava flow upon lava flow that erupted over 60 million years ago. Yet the whispers of these violent times still echo across the landscape. Rising dramatically from the plains of mid-Antrim, Slemish dominates the land for miles around. Slemish is what geologists call a volcanic plug. This oddly shaped hill is in fact the root of one of the volcanoes that fed the lava flows that now cover much of north-east Ireland. While eons of erosion by rain, ice and wind have removed the edifice of the once mighty volcano, today at Slemish we can still peer into the inside of the ancient volcano. The rock at Slemish is known as dolerite. It is related to basalt, but has much larger crystals that are visible to the naked eye, a sign that the molten rock, or magma, here cooled relatively slowly.

It is thought that St Patrick walked Slemish's slopes for six years after being taken into slavery at the age of 16. According to his writings, it was at Slemish that Ireland's patron saint turned to prayer as his only consolation. He escaped, became a priest and began his mission to convert the Irish to Christianity.

Causeway columns occur in the lower zone of the lava flow, while above them is a zone of thinner, less regular and often curved columns. This division is best seen at the feature known as the Giant's Organ, a few hundred metres to the east of the Causeway along the lower path.

How the Giant's Causeway formed

To understand how the spectacular columns formed we must thank a Russian geologist named Sergei Ivanovich Tomkeieff. In the 1930s he began working on the rocks of the Giant's Causeway. He noticed the variation in the distribution of columns within the Causeway flows. In a leap of imagination he found a convenient way of describing their appearance.

Tomkeieff compared the columns to the architectural structure of a classical Greek temple, where the roof or pediment is supported by rows of regular vertical columns called the colonnade and below the pediment is a decorated facade called the entablature.

Research carried out here and in other areas around the world where Causeway-type flows are found shows that they all share a common feature – while the thick lava flows were cooling their surface areas were flooded by water to form temporary lakes. The flood water could have been from heavy rainfall, or as in the case of the Causeway from rivers that existed before the eruption started.

When lava begins to cool it shrinks and polygon-shaped cracks form on the

The Giant's Eye at the Giant's Causeway is the result of weathering of the iron-rich basalt blocks, hence the rusty colour

surface; this is similar to the cracks in mud when it dries in the sun. The lava is losing heat upwards into the atmosphere and downwards into the ground, so these cracks work their way down through the flow from the top surface and upwards from the base. The regular columns of the Causeway show that the lower part of the flow cooled slowly and evenly to form the 'colonnade', but when the upper surface of the flow is flooded then the lava cools much more quickly, thus forming the more irregular, thinner columns of the 'entablature'.

The join between the colonnade and the entablature seen at the Giant's Organ is where the upward moving joints of the colonnade met the downward moving joints of the entablature when the flow was completely solidified. All parts of the jigsaw were now in place to present future generations of geologists with a fascinating scientific problem to unravel and a landscape that has featured in Irish mythology since earliest times.

Crushing pressures in the Ice Age

Following the volcanic eruptions during Palaeogene times, geological time moves first into the Neogene Period of Earth's history, which lasted from around 23 million to 2.6 million years ago, and then into the Quaternary, spanning the last 2.6 million years and up to the present day.

As it was a period of heavy erosion, no rocks from Neogene times remain in Northern Ireland, but by its end, the continents were roughly where they are now and global temperatures had begun to drop. Ice caps that had developed

At the Temple of Hephaestus, near the Acropolis in Athens, the columns supporting the roof are called the colonnade. The roof consists of the triangular pediment on top and the decorated entablature below that. Colonnade and entablature are now used to describe the pattern of columns at the Giant's Causeway

DID YOU KNOW?

Ailsa Craig is a small but prominent island in the Firth of Clyde between Antrim and Scotland, familiar to many travellers on the Northern Ireland–Scotland ferries. This island is formed of granite with a very distinctive blue speckled appearance, a bit like a thrush's egg. As the ice moved south from Scotland to engulf parts of eastern Ireland during the various stages of the Ice Age, it picked up pieces of this granite and deposited them in an 'erratic fan' down the east coast of Ireland. Ailsa Craig granite is the rock generally used in the manufacture of curling stones, the popular winter sport that involves rocks and ice.

At the Giant's Organ, Co. Antrim, the evenly-spaced wide columns of the colonnade pass up into the thinner, more irregular columns of the entablature

The modern day Greenlandic ice cap – much of the northern half of Ireland would have looked like this during the Ice Age

at the Earth's polar regions began to expand into lower latitudes. A third of the Earth's surface froze solid, including most of Ireland. The Ice Age, which heralded the dawn of the Quaternary, had arrived … and the scene was set for geological forces to work on large-scale environmental changes that have profoundly shaped the landscape and life of Earth.

During the Ice Age there was a periodic build-up of enormous continental ice sheets and mountain ice caps in many parts of the world. Over thousands of years the ice advanced and retreated many times. This deeply affected the whole of Ireland. Leaving in its wake landforms of every variety and size range, the ice made the final and most profound modifications to the Irish landscape and presented us with many of the sights we are familiar with today.

Each ice advance (called a glacial) lasted around 100,000 years, with warmer retreating periods (called interglacials) lasting around 10,000 to 60,000 years. During this time animals such as the woolly mammoth and woolly rhinoceros were alive – evidence of their existence has been found as fossils in Co. Antrim.

Ice sheets, ice caps and glaciers have immense bulldozing power to sculpt the surface of the Earth, both by removing and adding material. As ice moves over the bedrock, it picks up pieces of rock and incorporates them into its mass, making the ice a very effective grinder, eroder, scourer, scraper and gouger of anything it passes over. Eventually the ice drops the rock debris in its hold, either directly, to form deposits such as moraines and boulder clay, or indirectly, via meltwater streams to form beds of

MYTHOLOGY AND GEOLOGY

Glacial erratic, Easky, Co. Sligo

Erratics

Large rocks sitting on the northern landscape, as well as other geological oddities have built up their own folklore, with stories of gods, devils, giants and witches, all explaining why and where elements in the landscape look as they do. We now call these rocks 'glacial erratics' and know that they were left behind by the melting ice at the close of the last Ice Age. But close to the Sligo coast near the town of Easky lies a huge boulder. Now split in two, legend tells of how Finn McCool in a fit of temper threw the rock from the Ox Mountains to the south intending to hit the sea. His throw fell short of its target, which greatly worsened Finn's mood. He ran at the stone and angrily split it in two with his sword. In reality, this huge boulder did originate in the Ox Mountains, in accordance with the legend. But why it is split in two is still open to debate.

The landscape at Glenveagh National Park in Co. Donegal is typical of that left behind after the Ice Age, with many of the rock surfaces scraped bare by the ice and the valleys filled with sands and clays as the ice eventually melted and retreated

A fine example of a precariously perched granite block left behind by the Ice Age at Cloughmore, near Rostrevor, Co. Down

gravel, sand, silt or clay. To reach solid rock over most of Ireland you must dig through several metres of boulder clay. This in itself is witness to the huge effect ice has had on our landscape.

During the Ice Age, Ireland would have looked like modern-day central Greenland or Antarctica. Any exposed uplands would have been subject to the full powers of erosion by frost and ice and would often form jagged peaks referred to as nunataks. The familiar rugged outline of Slieve Binnian in the Mournes is likely to have formed in this way, as was its companion peak to the north, Slieve Bernagh.

Carving a landscape

The massive weight and power of the slow-moving ice was able to cut large, distinctive swathes through the landscape, leaving behind our celebrated u-shaped valleys. The ice carved many beauty spots in the northern landscape, including Glenariff, Co. Antrim; Glenfarne, Co. Leitrim; Glenelly, Co. Tyrone; Glenveagh, Co. Donegal; and the Annalong Valley in Co. Down.

Few would disagree that the sculpting effect of the ice on the landscape has been astounding, especially in scenic mountainous areas where the rock comes to the surface. These rugged glacial landscapes with their steep valley sides, waterfalls and scoured rock surfaces are very attractive to tourist, inhabitant, artist, poet and songster alike.

The many huge blocks of rock, often weighing several tons, scattered around the Irish countryside, show the immense power of ice to carry material over long distances. These great boulders, named glacial erratics, are pieces of rock that differ from the type of rock native to the area in which they rest.

The boulders were initially dropped on top of glacial ice as part of a rockfall or landslide, or else the ice plucked them up from the underlying bedrock. As the ice continued to move, they carried the boulders along. When the ice melted, these rocks were left in new locations. Over thousands of years, it is clear that much movement, much grinding, and much transport of erratics occurred. Aside from sparking myths and legends about giants, for example, glacial erratics can help to record the flow direction of glaciers.

Ice Age deposits left another important detail on Ireland – the multitude of low hills known as drumlins dotted over the landscape. From the Irish word '*droimnín*' meaning 'little hill', 'drumlin' is now used worldwide, to describe low, ice-moulded hills. The most striking examples are the swarm of oval-shaped drumlins of Co. Monaghan. But the northern part of Ireland is also known for its 'drumlin swarms' that extend from Co. Down to Cavan and into parts of Co. Longford, and can also be seen in Fermanagh and the Donegal Bay area.

Drumlins are usually about 300 metres long, perhaps 100 metres wide and up to 40 metres in height and occur in clusters. Viewed from a distance, as from the main Dublin–Belfast road near Newry, or at Strangford Lough, they present a rounded, rolling and subdued landscape with many small hills of near uniform height.

Mahee Island, Strangford Lough, Co. Down – the small islands in Strangford Lough are the tops of drumlins submerged by rising sea levels after the Ice Age

hill expanding the hollow into the deep corries we see today. The head walls of valleys such as the Poisoned Glen at Dún Lúiche (Dunlewey), Co. Donegal, for example, contain corries.

Another feature of retreating ice is that it leaves behind the accumulations of gravel, sand, silt or clay it had eroded and was carrying. When deposited, this material forms what is known as a moraine. The upper boundaries of moraines often mark the edges of usable farming land. Other deposits from after the Ice Age can also improve soil fertility. This can be seen in Co. Antrim at Glenariff where the 'ladder farms' stretch from the valley floor up the sides of the glen, giving each farming family, in theory, equal shares of the land. The lower step of the 'ladder' contains the more fertile soils on the valley floor, while the higher steps on the upper slopes held the more infertile soils.

Boulder clay and soil

Rock exposed to the power of nature eventually breaks down into soil. A typical soil may contain more than 50% of material derived from this breakdown of rocks, with the remainder made up of water, air and organic material known as humus.

Even in an era when few people are self-sufficient food producers, most are aware of how important the relatively thin layer of soil that covers the rock is to human survival. Soil types are many and varied. They are formed in a variety of ways, often from a complex mixture of materials from many sources. But the one thing they all have in common is that a proportion of their make-up

Drumlins influence land drainage, and therefore settlement patterns, and also make travel, navigation and transport harder. The labyrinth of drumlins and the lakes interspersed between them was one reason why the English found it difficult to take and control Ulster in the late sixteenth century. In the eyes of the celebrated geographer and

archaeologist E. Estyn Evans, the drumlin belts have also had a cultural influence in reinforcing the regional identity or 'personality' of Ulster.

Moraines and corries

Corries are armchair-shaped hollows found high up on the sides of mountains in Ireland. They often form on the shaded

and therefore colder side of hills. Here, as each glacial period got underway, snow would accumulate each winter but not melt away in the summer, eventually becoming compressed into ice, which, under the force of gravity, would start to move downhill as a glacier. As the ice moved it eroded backwards and downwards into the

The peaks of the Mourne Mountains, Co. Down, were subject to the full erosive powers of the ice

comes from the breakdown of the rocks making up the Earth's crust.

The great ice sheets of the last Ice Age crushed the outer layers of the Irish bedrock into boulders, cobbles, pebbles, sand, silt and clay. The mixture of the materials left behind when the ice melted is called boulder clay. Boulder clay covers much of the rock underlying the northern part of Ireland, and makes up the soil and subsoil we encounter when digging. Boulder clay is an important legacy of the Ice Age. It is a major component of many of our modern soils and it heavily influences the suitability of Irish soils for cultivation.

Coastal features
The end of the Ice Age was marked by sea level fluctuations as the vast ice sheets melted and the Earth's crust adjusted to the removal of the crushing weight of the ice caps, which were many kilometres thick in places. Over thousands of years this weight had

DID YOU KNOW?

Davagh Esker, Co. Tyrone

The railway line from Belfast to Dublin travels out from the northern city via Balmoral, along part of a natural embankment formed by an esker (a word originating from the Irish, *eiscir*, meaning ridge, and used by the international scientific community). Left around 13,000 years ago by waters draining the retreating ice at the end of the Ice Age, eskers are sands and gravels that were deposited on the Irish landscape in long ridges from streams and rivers that ran through and under the melting ice. Since they are numerous and often cross low and often boggy ground they have been an important influence on transport routes from earliest times. The main Cookstown–Omagh road follows the route of an esker, and other examples can be seen at Beragh, Co. Tyrone, or in the Sperrin and Foyle areas, where they are common. Besides affecting transport, eskers are a useful bequest to the construction industry. Eskers are an important modern-world source of 'sharp' sands and gravels. When mixing concrete, the bulk material, sand and gravel, must be sharp – the grains have to be angular to provide the maximum surface area to bind to the cement. Rounded and smooth sea sand would not do. Eskers provide sharpness because the glaciers tended to deposit their material quite soon after it was eroded, leaving little time for the sand and gravel grains to be worn away and rounded.

Glenariff, Co. Antrim, with its characteristic ladder farms, is a u-shape valley sculpted by ice

The power of nature

By about 420 million years ago, geological processes had established the rock foundation of Ireland as a jigsaw pattern of slabs, segments and fragments of the Earth's crust. It is rock of widely varying ages formed by continental rifting and ocean formation, caused by plate movement, as Ireland drifted from a position in the southern hemisphere, northwards and eastwards to its present location.

Since the literally Earth-shattering events of the early Palaeogene Period some 55–65 million years ago that produced the lavas of the Antrim Plateau and the granites of the Mournes, Ireland's geological environment has been intra-plate, that is, located away from plate edges. This means that Ireland has had no volcanic activity and no major earthquakes in the recent past.

The main landscape modifications in this period were the movement up or down of blocks of the Earth's crust along ancient fault lines, the erosion of uplifted areas pushed the crust down. After the ice melted the crust slowly began to rise. But since the rise in sea level due to the melting ice was faster than the rate at which the crust was lifting, for a short period the post-Ice Age seas were much higher than at present.

In Donegal and Antrim we can still see the evidence of the higher sea levels in land and seascape features such as raised beaches, sea stacks and arches, sea caves, and cliffs that are now well above the present high-water mark.

Following the retreat and eventual melting of the ice that had covered Ireland for so long, 13,000 years ago the arrival of warmer conditions set in motion a series of changes that would have a profound effect on the landscape and the flora and fauna of the area. The improvement in climate meant a massive immigration of new plants and animals across land-bridges from Britain and Europe. And one of the most significant landscape developments at this stage was the arrival of the first settlers.

Immediately after the Ice Age ended there was a brief period of higher sea levels. Evidence of this remains at Ballintoy, Co. Antrim, in the form of a low cliff face that was formed when the sea was at this higher level. It is now grassed over and set back from the present sea level

and the transport of the eroded material elsewhere.

One celebrated image of the north of Ireland clearly illustrates how time and the power of nature sculpted the landscape over the last 50 million years or so. From a height of over 850 m at Slieve Donard in south Co. Down, the Mourne Mountains, in the words of songwriter and entertainer Percy French, famously 'sweep down to the sea'.

The Mournes are granite, an igneous rock (see page 94), and the crystals in it are large (more than 2 mm in size generally). This means that the granite magma must have cooled slowly, and that it cooled at least several kilometres below the surface of Co. Down.

Although the Mournes rocks are around 55 million years old, the landscape they are part of in south Down is younger. Since the tops of the mountains are currently nearly 1 km above sea level, erosion must have taken off around 3 km of rock cover in the area in the last 55 million years to expose the granites that, deep in the Earth, were intruded as magma into the sandstones and mudstones of Co. Down.

This is the concept of denudation of the landscape, that is the removal of the outer layers of the Earth's crust to progressively expose the older material buried underneath. Rates of denudation for a moderate climate such as Ireland's are estimated to be around 10 mm to 100 mm per thousand years, depending on the composition of the rock. Rain,

sunshine, wind, frost, rivers, glaciers and ocean wave each have their own erosion affects.

A measure of weather

Weathering is the physical fragmentation and chemical decay of rocks and minerals *in situ* on the surface of the Earth. How fast the disintegration occurs depends on the original rock composition. The availability of water tends to accelerate the processes of mineral breakdown. But weathering varies with climate and depends on other factors such as whether tectonic forces are raising or lowering the land surface. Above all, weathering depends on time.

One way of measuring the rate at which weathering occurs is to look at a group of Celtic high crosses. These monuments

DID YOU KNOW?

High Cross, Clones, Co. Monaghan

The forces operating on the high crosses are the same forces that affect the outer surfaces of the Earth, that reduce mountains to plains with the resulting debris blown away in the wind or carried off by fast-flowing rivers carrying heavy loads of sand and mud. The cross at Clones was probably constructed in the tenth century AD and so the wear on the sculpture has occurred over a period of over 1,000 years. This process of weathering has become markedly accelerated over the last 30 years due to increased air pollution and is now of such concern that some crosses are being removed from their original locations or covered by protective cases to preserve them.

Affected by roughly 55 million years of erosion, Slieve Donard and the Mountains of Mourne 'sweep down to the sea' at Newcastle, Co. Down

Drumcliff High Cross, Co. Sligo. The poet W.B. Yeats is buried nearby in this churchyard

in the Irish landscape, sculpted mainly from sandstones, have been exposed to the rigours of the Irish climate for the last 1,000 years or so.

As free-standing artefacts on the landscape they eloquently illustrate the processes of interaction between the agents of weathering and the rocks they are carved from. Typically the crosses have elaborate biblical scenes carved on the head and four faces of their shafts. Depending on their age and the nature of the rock they are made from, many of these carvings show signs of wear and loss of detail as the rock is slowly worn away.

The wear is the result of the physical impact of the weather – the abrasive force of the wind, the erosive power of running water from heavy rain or the stresses induced by freezing and thawing, combined with the chemical effects of rain water, which is a dilute acid formed by absorbing carbon dioxide from the atmosphere.

The minerals that make up the common rock types in Ireland vary in their susceptibility to breakdown under atmospheric conditions. A mineral such as calcite, which makes up most of limestone, is very vulnerable to dissolving completely in rainwater. The sandstones from which many of the high crosses are carved mostly consist of grains of quartz, a very hard and resistant mineral, but these quartz grains are held together, or 'cemented' by calcite, which is vulnerable to the influence of the seemingly perpetual Irish rain.

When the binding calcite is dissolved out the quartz grains are loosened and are then liable to be washed or blown away by rain or wind, thus softening and rounding the edges of originally sharp and precise sculptures and carvings.

The same effect can be seen on statues and the inscriptions on very old gravestones, which can be impossible to read after several centuries of exposure to the elements.

Rock fragmentation

With some sandstones, the processes of weathering and decay are relatively simple: the chemistry involves only the dissolving of calcite in slightly acidic rainwater. In some other rocks, while the chemistry can be more complex, the end result is the same – a process of physical and chemical decay that leads to fragmentation. Fragmentation reduces rock masses into boulders, then into pebbles and then sand and finer particles. Its effects make the decreasing rock more susceptible to chemical weathering, which in turn leads to further fragmentation and so on.

A striking image of pioneer photographer of the Irish landscape, R.W. Welch, at Grey Man's Path at Fair Head, Co. Antrim, is a large-scale illustration of fragmentation.

Fair Head is what geologists call a sill (sills are horizontal 'intrusions' of magma into the adjacent rock and 'dykes' are vertical intrusions; 'intrusion' just means that the magma is injected under the Earth's surface). This sill, consisting of dolerite over 80 m thick, formed as molten magma moved into the surrounding rock some 55 million years ago. As it cooled it formed coarse, nearly vertical shrinkage cracks or joints. This jointing defines the very sharp vertical outline of Fair Head, but also affects the size and shape of the blocks that break off as the sill weathers. The fallen block used as a perch by Welch over 100 years ago is one of millions of rocks that have broken off from Fair Head. The pile of loose blocks, boulders and smaller pieces of rock that gather at the bottom of a cliff or steep slope like Fair Head is called a 'scree'.

A photograph of the same block over 100 years later shows no discernible change in the rocks on view, emphasising the very slow rate of weathering and fragmentation processes, even

Photographer R.W. Welch is perched dangerously on a block that has fallen from the Fair Head sill as a result of weathering processes

A similar view over 100 years later shows little discernible change in the rocks, indicating the very slow nature of weathering, even in the relatively harsh environment of the top of the Fair Head sill

The Fair Head sill showing the chaotic jumble of fallen blocks of the scree that makes traversing the base of the rocks so difficult

in a relatively harsh part of the Irish environment. A view of the scree clearly illustrates the chaotic and random nature of the jumble of blocks.

The rock making up Fair Head is similar to the basalts of the Antrim Plateau. In the case of Fair Head the dominant jointing is vertical, but in many of the lava flows making up the Antrim Plateau the shrinkage crack or joints can be in more than one direction and this too affects how the rock is weathered and broken down.

At Windy Gap at the Giant's Causeway there is basalt showing signs of deep weathering. Vertical and horizontal cracks in the rock have let in water, causing weathering to take place along these joints. This results in the formation of large blocks within the rock, with decay taking place from the outside of the block towards its centre.

The forces of physical and chemical decay can also fragment granite, the rock making up places such as the Mournes. Granites, like basalts, are igneous rocks, and they too shrink and crack when they cool, often with the same horizontal and vertical cracks as seen in basalt.

Granite consists mostly of two minerals: quartz and feldspar. Quartz is physically very resistant to wear, but feldspar, although quite a hard mineral when fresh, changes to soft clay when exposed to rainwater or groundwater and is easily washed out of the rock along the various cracks and joints. This causes the granite to fall apart and form small boulders, pebbles and sand grains. The clay formed by the breakdown of the feldspar can often be seen coating the boulders and pebbles, or carried in suspension by the streams and rivers, giving them a milky white colour.

Sediment transport
Following the slow weathering that breaks down rock to small fragments and clay particles, the processes of transportation take over. The material is carried by water, wind and ice to be deposited and then compressed elsewhere to form new sedimentary rocks such as sandstone, mudstone and limestone.

For instance, the distinctive red-brown sandstones of the Scrabo area around Newtownards, Co. Down, were deposited in a hot desert environment some 230 million years ago during Triassic times. The existence of ripple-marked surfaces within these sandstones suggests that they were laid down by shallow rivers and the presence of thin layers of mudstone shows that these rivers formed shallow lakes occasionally. Some of the sandstone grains are very well-rounded, an indication that they formed part of a desert dune being blown around this dry environment before eventually ending up in the river bed.

Legananny Dolmen, Co. Down

THE AXE FACTOR

Despite the immense forces that shaped the Earth's surface, today's landscape is the product of more than just blocks of the planet's rock fused together over, what Ireland's Nobel laureate for literature, Seamus Heaney, calls, 'the vastness and pastness' of time. The sights we see around us are the result of a complex series of interactions between nature – geology, biology and climate – acting together with human cultural and social activity.

Between the rocks and hard places that had formed by the end of the Ice Age, Stone Age humans, probably coming from Scotland, began to colonise the Irish landscape. The earliest evidence of human presence in Ireland after the retreat of the ice is between 9,000 and 10,000 years ago. The axe, the ever present tool of Stone Age culture, soon became not only a potent tool for the new settlers, but also a potent metaphor of the impact of humans on the landscape of Ireland and indeed elsewhere.

With axe in hand – or call it tractor or earth mover or oil rig in later ages – humankind's social, cultural and technological advances became significant agents of change on the natural environment. For instance, in Ireland, the introduction of farming around 6,000 years ago led to the clearance of the natural forest cover. That clearance came about because of new techniques that allowed the early settlers to make their axes more efficient.

An observer viewing Ireland from space in the years since the Stone Age people would have witnessed huge changes in the types of vegetation covering the rock framework of the country. The present orderly pattern of field boundaries and relatively sparse woodland cover is the result of human activity during only the last few hundred years.

It is easy to look now at the differences between the rural and urban environments and forget that the countryside is *not* the natural state. In fact, it is the result of the progress in society from a collector-hunter-scavenger existence to a cultivator-farmer state – a change that meant the domestication of animals and the cultivation of food crops for improved diet, health and increased security for an expanding population.

The impacts on the Irish landscape associated with the arrival of the earliest

> **" A geologist is a fault-finder. "**
>
> **Anon**

DID YOU KNOW?

Mount Sandel, Coleraine, Co. Londonderry

Radiocarbon dates at Mount Sandel in Co. Londonderry indicate that the site is one of the earliest human occupations in Ireland and was first occupied around 9,000 years ago. These earliest settlers lived in circular huts built from saplings, about 6 m across with central fireplaces. There is evidence to suggest an abundant food supply ranging from salmon in the summer and wild pig in winter, with a range of berries, nuts and fruit in the autumn. Stone tools recovered from the site include flint axes, needles, scalene triangle-shaped microliths, pick-like tools, backed blades and a very few hide scrapers. Almost all the artefacts found were flint. Essential to the Mount Sandel settlement, which overlooks the estuary of the Lower Bann river, the flint was probably collected from a shingle beach or river bed. Smaller quantities were collected from screes at the foot of chalk cliffs, a few removed from the chalk itself. The settlers would have gathered most of the flint from within 10 km of the site, probably at either Portrush in Co. Antrim or Downhill in Co. Londonderry.

settlers – a continually expanding population, coupled with the development of agriculture – led to huge changes in Ireland from the Stone Age through the Bronze Age, Iron Age and into the early-Christian era and medieval times.

The advent of industrialisation in the nineteenth century and increasingly mechanised farming techniques accelerated profound changes in areas such as settlement patterns, the development of farms and villages and more substantial towns and cities. Over time a cultural landscape has evolved that carries the marks of many generations of settlers. All of this has had an effect on the natural environment, including the number of plant and animal species on the island and the extent to which the landscape changed from how it looked when it finally reappeared from under the ice.

Generally, human forces impose landscape adjustments on top of the slower, natural changes to the environment that occur like the gradual climate change that took place after the Ice Age, or the spread of blanket bog over much of Ireland, which started around 6,000 years ago.

But do people dominate our landscape? There is a view among many who study the various aspects of landscape that the regional diversity of Ireland is primarily a product of the inhabitants who have imposed their culture on the environment. More than geology or climate, their argument runs, it is people who are the prevailing influence.

Actually, landscape is the interface between the natural environment and humans. The rock, modified by climate and

biology, interacts with the aesthetic and cultural influences of its inhabitants and the impact of their social and technological advancements. There is no doubt that people and their cultures and technologies are a major force in landscape evolution, even, too, on the state of the planet today.

But the shape of our landscape comes from rock types and tectonic structure, on variations in the hardness of rocks and their ability to resist erosion, on the faulting patterns cut on the fabric of the Earth's crust. So despite the changes brought about by 'axe carrying' humans of whatever era, whether it be deforestation, arable farming, the laying of a new motorway, the construction of a skyscraper building or the triggering of global warming, the uplands remain uplands, the lowlands remain lowlands and Lough Neagh remains Lough Neagh, with all the restrictions these landscape shapes impose on humans using them.

In the end, geology governs how people use the landscape and what they can do on it, and so is *the* primary and dominant influence on the landscape, in spite of the impact of human culture.

The geology of the Stone Age

The term Stone Age is a description of the earliest recognised cultures of the prehistoric period, the time before history was written down. In reality it covers three ages: the Palaeolithic, Mesolithic and Neolithic, or, old, middle and new Stone Age.

But an archaeologist probably coined the term. A geologist would never use

DID YOU KNOW?

Neolithic flints from Co. Antrim, including arrow and javelin point, hollow scrapers and a knife

The Neolithic tool-fashioning technique was known as 'knapping' and required great patience and skill. They chipped flakes off the flint or chert using a variety of methods, depending on whether they were shaping out the rough axe head for finer finishing later or making the final finished tool or weapon. For weapons, small slivers of flint could be inserted into the end of a shaft of wood to form arrow or harpoon points or barbs. The most typical tools were flint microliths, small splinters or blades of flint that were fashioned into a number of different shapes – scalene triangles, rods or needle points.

the word 'stone' to describe the versatile and hard-wearing materials that humans have used over millennia for a wide range of utensils, tools and weapons. The materials are of course naturally occurring minerals and rocks.

Mineral and rock resources like flint, chert, sandstone and basalt had a profound effect on the physical and cultural landscape of Ireland in prehistoric times. Their availability to our ancestors at crucial points in Stone Age evolution and beyond has

strongly influenced social and cultural development on the island. In turn, social, cultural and technological progress has impacted back on the natural environment through the exploitation of the landscape's natural geological resources.

The earliest minerals exploited in Ireland by the Mesolithic settlers were flint and its variation chert. They were essential for the manufacture of the earliest tools and therefore for the survival and spread of the earliest settlements.

Flint, as a form of the mineral quartz, is harder than steel and fractures easily to give razor-sharp edges. A narrow zone around the Antrim Plateau in the north-east is Ireland's only source of flint *in situ*, although because it is so hard and durable it is abundant along the shoreline and in boulder clay.

It is no coincidence that archaeologists have found some of the earliest tangible evidence of Mesolithic activity in Ireland in Co. Antrim. Also many of the later Mesolithic sites are along the coast, particularly along the raised beach coast of Antrim, which had a ready supply of flint.

Chert has the same chemical composition as flint and many similar properties. It is mainly found in the limestones formed in Carboniferous times, for example around the Fermanagh lakes, south Donegal and Sligo. The early settlers used it in the same way as flint.

Moving in relatively small extended family groups, the Mesolithic people used their flint tools – and bone, wood and antler – to hunt deer, wild boar, game fowl and perhaps even bear. They gathered fruits, nuts, wild cereal crops and fungi from the dense woodland covering the landscape. Thanks to their exploitation of their natural resources, and far from the primitive caveman stereotype, these people managed to thrive.

The landscape the Mesolithic people inherited from the Ice Age was pristine or unaltered. They made only minor changes to it. It was in Neolithic times, with the growth of agriculture and farming, that the beginning of the transformation of the natural Irish landscape came about.

Chalk beds in Antrim showing layers of flint in the form of small rounded nodules

The Céide Fields, Co. Mayo, where the removal of the peat bog uncovered a complete array of stone field walls, farm houses and megalithic tombs

Fine axe factories

The Neolithic age marked the first great modification of the Irish landscape by human activity. The introduction of farming brought permanent changes to the environment – extensive forest clearances, new forms of social organisation and the division of the land into fields and animal enclosures. Archaeologists have uncovered the everyday lives of the Neolithic people in places such as the Céide Fields site in Co. Mayo, the oldest known field system in the world. The site includes the remains of stone field walls, farmsteads and megalithic tombs, revealing a farming people living in a highly organised peaceful community.

The clearing of the wooded landscape to permit farming required a more complex set of tools than those used by the Mesolithic people. Specialist axes were now required. The Neolithic people realised that axes made from flint and other rock types were not up to the job and it appears they put more emphasis on rock types that required more preparation and therefore a much more sophisticated production process. This led to the development of polished stone axe-heads. Polishing increases an axe's strength, and makes it less easily damaged and longer lasting than the flaked edge of a flint axe.

It is clear the Neolithic people had the abilities of modern-day exploration geologists and manufacturing industrialists. Their skill at producing polished stone axes shows they had a finely tuned knowledge of their landscape and environment. Using a variety of techniques and materials from many

DID YOU KNOW?

The red laterite layer underneath basalt lava, Co. Antrim

The porcellanite craved by our ancestors to make their fine axes came into being when the distinctive red soil, laterite, came into contact with magma and was baked at temperatures of more than 1,200°C. This was the equivalent of firing clay in a potter's kiln and the soft clay minerals of the laterite were changed to hard minerals such as corundum, a commonly used abrasive. In appearance the laterite is changed to a blue-coloured rock with a porcelain-like appearance, hence the name porcellanite.

localities, they were able to make axes efficient enough to clear the forests as they gradually adopted an agricultural lifestyle.

The dominant material used in axe manufacture was a rock called porcellanite, a hard rock capable of sustaining a sharp edge and taking a high polish. The two known locations of porcellanite in Ireland were in Co. Antrim: Tievebulliagh, near Cushendun, and Brockley on Rathlin Island, north of Ballycastle. Both sites were remote from the main areas of settlement at the time and we can only speculate on whether they were found by accident or as a result of a systematic search.

Well over half of the axes manufactured in Ireland come from the two porcellanite quarry sources in Co. Antrim. Axe heads that originate from these axe factories were exported across Ireland and Britain, from the Outer Hebrides in Scotland to the south coast of England. Flakes, rejects and part-finished axes can still be found at Tievebulliagh. No finished axes have been found, indicating that the axes were roughed out here before being completed elsewhere.

The exploration of the countryside to find porcellanite, the manufacture of the axe heads on site or in a separate location, and then the distribution of the finished products over virtually the whole of Ireland and the export of axes into Britain is the earliest example of large-scale use of a natural resource in the history of the island.

Special axes from special places

Within Neolithic society axes became more than wood-cutting tools, significant though that was. A wide variety of different rock types was used as axes including shale, sandstone and a variety of igneous rocks. Axes had value and could be traded and exchanged. Many finely worked, high-status axes have been found. They may never have been intended for use except in ceremonies and in the giving of gifts, helping to form alliances between communities.

The axe became a prized cultural artefact during the Neolithic age and the manufacture of stone axes became a significant cultural activity. Also, the exposures of rock that the raw material came from became special places within the landscape – a perfect example of the blending of the physical and cultural landscapes.

The complete process of axe manufacture, from exploration to extraction of the valuable raw material, from roughing out to final polishing to distribution, forged links within Neolithic society. There is evidence of an active interchange between these Irish axes and their equivalent made from a rock called tuff coming from localities in Britain. The trading activity established connections with other parts of Ireland and further afield in Britain and Europe.

But what was it about porcellanite axes that apparently made them so much more than implements for cutting down trees? While the rocks from the two source locations, Brockley and Tievebulliagh, are indistinguishable in appearance, recent detailed work on their chemical composition has shown small but

significant differences in certain trace elements. This shows that the Rathlin site was at least as important as the relatively more accessible Tievebulliagh site. This raises the question of why the more hazardous site would be used as much as the site which would presumably have presented less danger in finding and removing the raw material.

Interestingly, the only other important axe production site in Neolithic Ireland was also off-shore. Lambay Island, in Co. Dublin, was a significant source of stone axes that used a fine-grain igneous rock known as Lambay porphyry to produce very distinctive looking axes. It seems that islands were highly significant for the Neolithic people as sources of the raw material for their axes. The apparent link between 'place' and axe production is the idea that the location of the source of the raw material was as important as the quality of the material, all other things being equal.

Axe production in Neolithic north-west England, at Pike of Stickle in Cumbria, supports this idea. Below the summit on the south-eastern side of the Pike O'Stickle hill in the English Lake District, Neolithic workers quarried and roughly shaped a distinctive volcanic rock called greenstone into axe blanks or roughs that were then traded around the country. The scree slope that runs from near the top of Pike O'Stickle is the spoil from axe quarrying activities. Tests of the rock from the Pike O'Stickle locality shows that rock of equal suitability to that taken from the inaccessible areas was available at lower levels but was ignored in favour of the rock at the high and therefore dangerous levels.

Characteristic jointing in the granite tors, Slieve Binnian, Co. Down

Rathlin Island, Co. Antrim, was the site of an important source of the porcellanite rock used in the making of polished axes in Neolithic times – island sources were regarded as special places

Tievebulliagh, Co. Antrim. The hard dark blue porcellanite is seen in contact with the brownish dolerite

The hard, brittle porcellanite was probably extracted by first using fire to heat the rock, then chilling it with water to cause the rock to fracture, thus allowing workable blocks to be extracted from the outcrop. To minimise the carrying of heavy loads of quarried porcellanite it seems that blocks were shaped into the general form of an axe on site at Tievebulliagh. These 'rough-outs' were manufactured, possibly by using quartzite hammer stones, with final shaping and polishing using hard sandstones and quartz sand as an abrasive in 'axe factories' elsewhere.

An axe production site near the summit of Tievebulliagh, Co. Antrim, where axe 'rough-outs' were produced

From the evidence available from the sites of stone axe production in Ireland and Britain it appears that these axe sites were often located in spectacular but generally inaccessible places that may well have been hazardous to reach. It seems the character of the place was at least as important to Neolithic man as the qualities of the rock extracted. High ground and steep gradients or off-shore location helped to isolate these preferred localities from the sphere of everyday activity.

The pattern is that the stone axe heads that were circulated over wide areas through exchange are visually very distinctive. This seems to be the special axe factor that Neolithic people craved.

A land transformed

After the Neolithic age traditional farming methods continued more or less unchanged for thousands of years. There was a steady decline in woodland cover and the gradual clearing and cultivation continued. The number of plant and animal species also declined as more and more environments were destroyed by an increased pressure on land for agricultural use and the economic requirements of intensive farming practices.

Since it was uncovered by the melting ice for the last time about 13,000 years ago it is possible to plot the changes that must have occurred in Ireland's topography as the landscape passed from Arctic-like tundra, through the Stone Age and subsequent periods, to the scenery we are familiar with today.

Around 12,000 years ago, as the climate warmed after the Ice Age, the country was as yet without a population. There was grass and bushes on the lowlands, but little vegetation on the hill slopes. Post-glacial lakes were large and numerous.

By around 8,000 years ago, with an increasingly warmer climate the entire landscape was covered by deciduous woodland, thinning out towards the higher ground. This is the Mesolithic period and the earliest settlers may have formed

Dusk on the Canadian tundra. The Irish landscape would have resembled this after the ice finally retreated around 13,000 years ago

DID YOU KNOW?

Part of a hoard of Neolithic porcellanite axes found at Malone, near Belfast

Porcellanite axes from Rathlin and Brockley have been found in virtually every county in Ireland, with the greatest concentration, not surprisingly perhaps, in the north-east. When considering the range of rock types used in the manufacture of stone axes in Ireland it is striking that porcellanite is by far the dominant rock type used. Well over half the known examples are made from this material, which can be found in only two relatively small outcrops. This dominance may reflect the quality of the material – porcellanite axes were very efficient at doing what axes are required to do – but it may also be an indication of the enhanced status of porcellanite axes due to the relative rarity of the material and its very different appearance compared to axes made from commoner, more mundane sedimentary rocks. The further from source, the more exotic the axe would have seemed and therefore the greater its status. The axes' distribution also shows that a network of contacts existed at this stage of Neolithic society, along which the axes were moved from their sources in north-east Ireland.

Blanket peat bog on the flanks of Cuilcagh Mountain, straddling the border between Cavan and Fermanagh

Ness Wood, Co. Londonderry – much of Ireland would have been covered by woodland like this before the advent of agriculture and the subsequent tree clearance

Experiments by archaeologists replicating stone axes with ground edges show that trees with diameters of around 15 cm can be chopped down in approximately 20 minutes, without noticeable damage to the edge of the axe. At this rate of felling, tree clearance for agricultural purposes was clearly feasible in Neolithic times. Stone axes are still used for this purpose today by certain Pacific tribes.

small clearings along rivers and by the seashore for their camps.

Some 5,500 years ago, the Neolithic period, agriculture had started and the earliest farmers had begun clearing woodland to allow grazing and cultivation. Upland areas were used for rough grazing and large burial cairns were built on the summits. Lake basins were progressively filled by natural peat growth. There is evidence of extensive field systems based on stone-walled enclosures used probably for the management of cattle, probably from around 5,500 years ago – the Céide Fields in Co. Mayo was uncovered from beneath a peat bog that developed about 4,500 years ago. Here the growth of peat has performed a useful function in preserving important early evidence of Neolithic farming practices.

Metal-working was introduced to Ireland around 4,500 years ago and by the end of the Bronze Age 2,500 years ago the hill areas had been completely cleared of woodland and on the summits the

'Lazy beds' in the Glenelly Valley, Sperrins, seen as parallel ridges in one of the fields to the right and below the ruined cottage. They were used to produce crops from poor quality soils and the picture illustrates the height at which crops were grown in the nineteenth century, compared with today when the land is exclusively used for sheep farming

Sods of cut peat drying in Co. Donegal

woodland was replaced by blanket peat bogs. On the lowlands woodland clearance for cattle-grazing continued with cultivation declining because of renewed climatic deterioration.

In the early Christian period around 1,200 years ago population growth and expansion of farming led to widespread environmental changes. Ringforts were built as settlements with surrounding small fields and extensive open grazing in woodland clearances. The uplands remained open with extensive bog

coverage. By around 400 years ago, at the beginning of seventeenth century, it is estimated that tree cover in Ireland was diminished to the extent that woodland cover accounted for no more that 12.5%, and may have been as low as 2%, of the land area.

In the period before the Great Famine in the 1840s the lowlands and many upland areas were densely settled and the farmland sub-divided by regular, enclosed fields and woodland was extremely sparse.

Small farms were multiplying on the hill slopes and bogs.

The present-day landscape has seen rural depopulation from about the mid-nineteenth century with many smallholdings disappearing and the remaining farms and fields enlarged. Grassland is now the dominant land use. The lowland and upland bogs have been reduced in size with new coniferous forests established on abandoned hill farms and lowland bogs.

Around 7,000 years ago tree cover was at its maximum but then a wetter climate in Ireland provided conditions that favoured the growth of peat bogs over much of the country. It is likely that the early settlers helped this change to the landscape as they cleared trees as they developed and expanded agriculture. Their activities account for the range of things buried in peat bogs, from tree stumps and roots, to stone circles such as at Beaghmore in Co. Tyrone or a complete field system discovered under the peat at the Céide Fields in Co. Mayo.

Farm clusters in Co. Donegal showing the remains of nineteenth century settlement patterns

A modern agricultural landscape in lowland areas

Giant's Ring, Co. Down

PROMINENT MONUMENTS

The Neolithic age left great marks on the island of Ireland. The upland forests were cleared for farmland. Cattle, sheep and goats were imported into the country for the first time. The population grew. But another striking and landscape-changing mark of the age was the appearance and dramatic spread of megaliths.

There are more than 1,500 megaliths (from the Greek *mega*, great, and *lithos*, stone) located around the Irish landscape, the majority of them in the north and west. These great stones were erected for a variety of purposes, including reminders of past events, territory markers, and as part of the spiritual, religious and ceremonial beliefs and rituals in the society that constructed them. Megaliths were used either on their own or with other stones to construct

> **❛❛ Geology, perhaps more than any other department of natural philosophy, is a science of contemplation. It demands only an enquiring mind and senses alive to the facts almost everywhere presented in nature. ❜❜**
>
> **Sir Humphrey Davy**
> **Eminent British chemist and inventor of the miner's safety lamp (1778-1829)**

Giant's Ring, Ballynahatty, near Belfast, a portal dolmen with henge or circular bank

various types of monument. Types of megalith include stone circles, standing stones, cairns, henges, and burial mounds and chambers.

The selection, movement and setting up of these very large stones, and their extremely precise alignment to the sun in some cases, shows that the builders responsible had substantial skill not just in organising the labour, but in the mechanics and mathematics of architectural and engineering forces and frictions. Megaliths reveal that the people of Neolithic times were not only making significant changes to the physical Irish landscape, but viewing their surroundings differently and integrating them into their lives in a more complex way.

There are clear differences in the scale of the monuments erected in Neolithic times. Some, such as the highly visible cairn (a monument or landmark) known as Maeve's Tomb on top of the hill of Knocknarea in Co. Sligo, were clearly meant to dominate the surrounding area, and still do so today. But others, such as the circular bank and tomb at the Giant's Ring near Belfast at Ballynahatty in Co. Down, were on a lesser scale. Smaller-scale megaliths such as passage graves or portal tombs were often about making an impact at a local level.

Underlying geology

How did Neolithic communities choose megalith sites? What was it about the locations, the rocks and the landscape that made their sites so special or sacred? Evidence from archaeologists suggests that many of the sites showed signs of human activity before the Neolithic communities modified them by adding a megalith. The significance of sites seemingly often post-dated the society that constructed the monuments. It appears likely that megalith building in the Neolithic age was just one phase in a complex and prolonged history in the area of the sites.

There is also abundant evidence that Neolithic communities had a clear grasp of the geology, and the component parts and features of the landscape they were living in. Their understanding of the significance of certain minerals and rock types such as flint and porcellanite for the functions of everyday living

The view from the slopes of Slieve Gullion over the Ring of Gullion, Co. Armagh

passed over into the use of these and other materials in cultural and religious activities. Their building of circular monuments to reflect the circular aspect of the surrounding landscape is another example, as shown at Beltany in Co. Donegal and in examples from Britain such as the Ring of Brodgar in the Orkney Islands in Scotland. Again, when decorating the UNESCO World Heritage Site at Newgrange monument at Brú na Bóinne, Co. Meath, the builders used what they would have considered 'exotic' Wicklow quartz and Mourne granite. Their use of materials from outside the immediate area probably indicates a Neolithic desire to incorporate the wider geography of a region into a local monument that was clearly of great cultural significance.

The apparent compulsion to make an impression on the landscape perhaps indicates how the Neolithic people viewed the integration of the physical and cultural landscapes, both of which were evolving, and how they had begun to view themselves in a time continuum that embraced not just their ancestors, but also future generations.

An obvious feature of many of their sites is high visibility, and this draws many parallels between the Neolithic age and contemporary and recent history. In sites and localities such as Slemish in Co. Antrim, Scrabo Hill in Co. Down, the Ring of Gullion in Co. Armagh or Knocknarea in Co. Sligo, people still consider the 'place' as significant.

Of course, the position such sites take in the landscape is due to the underlying bedrock geology and their exposure to the forces of erosion and denudation. The Ring of Gullion's circular arrangement of hills is entirely due to its origin as a geological feature known as a ring dyke, a circular fracture or fault under a volcano that may be filled with magma. The dominant Slemish Mountain in mid-Antrim, long a place of pilgrimage associated with Saint

Creevykeel megalithic tomb, Co. Sligo

There are four major types of megalithic tombs. 1) Court cairns are shaped in a long mound with a forecourt at one end leading into a long and often sub-divided chamber. A good example is at Creevykeel, Co. Sligo. 2) Portal tombs or portal chambers such as found at the Giant's Ring just outside Belfast at Ballynahatty, Co. Down, consist of a number of upright stones covered by one or more capstones and sometimes placed in a long or round mound. The term portal tomb is now used to describe what was previously known as a dolmen. 3) Passages tombs are round mounds having a burial chamber roughly in the centre, which is reached by a passage leading from the edge of the mound. These are best illustrated by the Carrowkeel complex in Co. Sligo (see page 56). 4) Wedge tombs have long rectangular chambers usually roofed with large stones and placed in a long wedge-shaped mound. The chamber tends to rise in height towards the front. Good examples can be found at Loughash, Co. Tyrone, or at Tireighter, Co. Londonerry.

Patrick, owes its shape and aspect to a lava lake that sat below the summit of a large volcano some 60 million years ago. The natural formation of Scrabo Hill is of sandstone with a capping of a harder igneous rock, dolerite. The harder rock has protected the softer sandstone underneath from the ravages of erosion, particularly during the Ice Age, leaving the hill prominent in the local landscape.

From earliest times up to the present the desire of societies to modify the landscape by adding structures that seem permanent has endured. As recently as 1999 the muscle power of 1,000 young people erected the Strangford Stone in Co. Down, now the tallest single standing stone, or monolith, in Ireland, to mark the new millennium. This slab of Mourne granite continued the exploits of monument making several thousand years after standing stones were first introduced to the Irish landscape.

Scrabo Tower, Newtownards, Co. Down. The scars from the sandstone quarries are clearly visible on the south flank of Scrabo Hill

DID YOU KNOW?

Can geology tell us anything about Queen Maeve, the legendary ruler of Connacht? Megalithic monuments are an important part of the landscape in Ireland, and none more so than those set in the breathtaking countryside around Carrowmore, Co. Sligo. These monuments include the renowned Maeve's Cairn, traditionally claimed as the tomb of the first-century Celtic royal. The cairn, in which Maeve is said to be buried standing up in her armour and with her sword facing her enemies in Ulster, dominates the skyline and caps the hill of Knocknarea. The scenery in this part of Sligo shows a clear relationship with the underlying geology. But while archaeological surveys of the area's megalithic monuments have been carried out in recent years, geological aspects of their construction, such as the rock types used and their sources, have been neglected. Now geologists hope to redress that imbalance. They intend to look at the main rock types used in some of the monuments by examining the particular characteristics and the likely sources of the blocks used in their construction.

Queen Maeve's Grave, Co. Sligo

At more than 10 m high the Millennium Strangford Stone in Delamont Country Park, Co. Down, is the highest megalith in Britain or Ireland, weighs more than 25 tonnes and was quarried in the Mournes

Houses of the dead

In the northern half of the country there is a high density of megalithic tombs that are probably the most obvious marker of the spread of prehistoric ritual and culture in Ireland. These landscape-dominating monuments remain as the surviving markers in a complex array of symbols relating to territory, tribal allegiance and ancestry.

You do not need to erect massive stone tombs just to bury the dead. So these tombs were clearly places of symbolic, religious and ceremonial importance to the Neolithic population. In most of the tombs that have been excavated archaeologists have found human remains – usually, but not always, cremated. Grave goods such as pottery, arrowheads, beads, pendants and axes have also been discovered.

The design and construction of the megalithic tombs indicate the development of a more complex social structure capable of organising the communal effort required for such huge undertakings. In fact, there is still debate among archaeologists as to whether the spread of agriculture acted as a trigger for the building of megaliths, or whether the two processes proceeded in parallel.

The important point is that both the development of agriculture and the building of megalithic tombs represented a radical change from what had been the norm for society before. The population was changing how it viewed nature. Rituals were evolving. The natural physical landscape was now something that could be modified and moulded for the benefit of society.

It seems the changes in social organisation that were taking place allowed the development of an increasingly sophisticated megalithic architecture that involved placing huge rocks in the landscape so as to be visible over great distances.

Adding stone monuments to places regarded as important or different reflects changes in the early dwellers' views of landscape and their concept of place. Ritual and symbolism was important, and it was apparent not just in the presence of the monument, but also in its location in the landscape, its physical relationship to other monuments, the rocks used and its internal structures and features.

Carrowmore and Carrowkeel

Two prime localities for megalithic tombs are in Co. Sligo. Carrowmore, the largest and most important megalithic complex in Europe, and Carrowkeel, probably one of the most important centres in ancient Ireland, are vital in understanding the evolving ritual landscape.

The scenery in Sligo is spectacular and shows a clear relationship with the underlying geology. The main group of rocks in Sligo are about 330 million years old. They are sedimentary rocks, Carboniferous in age, and in this part of Ireland they are mostly limestones and sandstones. They tend to form impressive flat-topped hills and steep cliff faces such as Benbulben or the cliffs above Lough Glencar.

But to the south and east of Sligo there is a band of much older metamorphic rocks forming the Ox Mountains. These are among the oldest rocks in Ireland at around 1,000 million years old. They form a peak-filled, rugged skyline – a marked contrast to the flat-top hills of the limestone country around them. These rocks are mostly schists and gneisses – hard, quartz-rich rocks.

West of Sligo city, capping the hill of Knocknarea, is the highly visible Maeve's Cairn, traditionally hailed as the tomb of first-century Queen Maeve of Connacht. Actually, the cairn is probably several thousand years older and linked to the burial monuments at Carrowmore, some 5 km away to the east, from where the cairn is clearly visible.

Within this setting the Carrowmore cemetery is a visually dominant cluster of some 40 megaliths covering an area of about 4 sq km. The tombs are arranged in the form of an oval, usually facing and surrounding a central monument, which is a large cairn c alled Listoghil.

The surviving stone monuments are predominantly metamorphic rocks – similar to the schist and gneiss of the Ox Mountains. The only apparent exception is Listoghil. It consists of a square-shaped chamber and the remains of a cairn, with a large roof

The rugged peaks of the Ox Mountains in Co. Sligo, formed of some of the oldest rocks on the Irish mainland

slab. The roof slab is unusual in that it is limestone, probably from the immediate area around Carrowmore.

The metamorphic material used to form the upright stones and caprocks at Carrowmore may well have been present in the area in Neolithic times as glacial erratics – blocks torn from the rocks of the Ox Mountains by glaciers or ice sheets and dumped on top of the limestone of north Co. Sligo.

But this does not quite explain why the Neolithic people chose gneiss for the uprights at Carrowmore. Gneisses are quartz-bearing, which can glitter in sunlight, and quartz appears to have been highly prized. Perhaps they used gneiss because it was convenient and plentiful. Perhaps they used limestone for the capstone on the biggest tomb for engineering reasons – the nearby limestone is capable of supplying a much larger block of stone than provided by the gneiss erratics used elsewhere on the site. Whatever the motives for the selections made by the people who constructed these monuments, it is clear they had a very good grasp of the differences in texture, appearance, properties and locations of the main rock types in their area.

The monument builders must have intended some form of visual relationship between the tombs at Carrowmore and Queen Maeve's Tomb at Knocknarea and Benbulben, because it is also possible to view the Carrowmore tombs in an even

The view towards Knocknarea and Queen Maeve's Grave from the Carrowmore megalithic cemetery, Co. Sligo

broader landscape context. Maeve's Tomb has its maximum visibility from the east. The builders must have designed it to be viewed from that side.

Each of the Ox Mountain peaks is associated with a summit (passage) tomb or cairn, and with two further conspicuous cairns on the top of Cairns Hill to the east of Carrowmore the peaks mark the passage of the sun through the sky. This means that the builders used tombs or cairns to mark hills to the east and south, but not on hills to the north, such as Benbulben.

The contrasting topography – the flat-topped hills, the more jagged peaks and

the hill at Carrowmore, from which five counties are visible – appear to have some kind of alignment and interplay related to the local geology and landscape. Also, it would appear that the sun rises over one of the Ox Mountain cairns and casts a shadow from the pointed upright at the front of the Listoghil burial chamber on 31 October every year (the Celtic festival of Samhain – beginning of winter), and again on 1 February (Imbolc – beginning of spring). It is unlikely that this was all haphazard. Interestingly, these festivals are Celtic and therefore post-date the tombs at Carrowmore by several millennia. Is this perhaps an example of pre-existing dates of

significance being adopted by the Celtic people just as, in turn, Christianity later adopted the same dates into All Saint's Day (1 November) and St Bridget's Day (1 February)?

It would seem that the builders designed and placed many of these tombs with the objective of constructing new landscape perspectives, often by using rock types different from the local bedrock. For example, they used metamorphic rock almost exclusively for the uprights in the Carrowmore complex, which sits on a limestone bedrock. A similar contrast occurs at the Giant's Ring, near Belfast, where the stones of the tomb are composed of

Scrabo dolerite, which is only available some 15 km away near Scrabo Hill.

Some Neolithic monuments also appear to have been constructed in sympathy with the existing landscape features. At the Bricklieve Mountains, Co. Sligo, there is another major megalithic cemetery at Carrowkeel, seemingly oriented towards Carrowmore.

Unlike Carrowmore, the rocks used here appear to be entirely from the local area, comprising mostly limestones with occasional reddish-brown sandstone boulders. The Carrowkeel bedrock is limestone and a number of the tombs appear to have been constructed with this, seemingly to be in harmony with the surroundings and deliberately to fit in with the contours of the immediate topography. In other monuments, however, there can be a striking and discordant effect, as in that produced by the magnificent Kilclooney portal tomb in Co. Donegal.

The locations of these structures therefore strive to communicate the power of the locality, and very often their form echoes the form of the landscape around it, thereby embodying the countryside within the structure. Whether on a prominent height or incorporating natural features and materials into the structure itself, it appears the surrounding natural landscape is deliberately being evoked.

Circles inside circles

A later Neolithic development, following the building of megalithic tombs, was the erection of stone circles, stone rows and standing stones. In Ireland there are two main concentrations, one in south Munster, the other in mid-Ulster, with important examples located at Beaghmore, Co. Tyrone, Ballynoe, Co. Down and Beltany, Co. Donegal.

The Beltany Stone Circle, located about 2 km south-west of the village of Raphoe in Co. Donegal, is composed of 60 stones although it is thought there were originally many more. There is a single stone outside the circle. Considered one of the finest examples of a stone circle in Ulster, it has been the subject of much archaeological study and speculation over the years. Geological aspects of the structure, including the nature and distribution and sources of the rock types making up the stones of the monument, have not yet been fully studied, but the circle can certainly be viewed in the context of the surrounding countryside. The upright stones making up this circle are all metamorphic rocks, generally medium-coarse grained schists, tending to have quartz and mica as the dominant minerals.

The Kilclooney More portal tomb, Co. Donegal, clearly designed to produce a striking and discordant effect on the landscape

Cairn and passage tomb at Carrowkeel in the Bricklieve Mountains, Co. Sligo. Monuments in this complex appear to be in harmony with the immediate landscape, fitting in with the contours of the surrounding topography

DID YOU KNOW?

The Beaghmore Stone Circles, Co. Tyrone

The Beaghmore Stone Circles in Co. Tyrone is one of the most extensive stone complexes in Ireland. It consists of three pairs of stone circles, a series of stone alignments and a number of small stone cairns. The remarkable feature about this complex is that until the late 1930s, when it was discovered, it lay hidden under the all-enveloping peat bog, which had covered so much of the country since the Neolithic people had erected the monuments around 4,000 years ago.

The Beaghmore Stone Circle complex, Co. Tyrone, is one of the best known assemblages in Ireland, covering a site of around two hectares (five acres)

The single standing stone outside the Beltany Stone Circle, Co. Donegal

The single outside stone of the Beltany Stone Circle in south Donegal is quite different from all the other stones in the circle. When freshly erected it would have appeared dark green with white speckles and probably came from Croaghan Hill, around 5 km away from the site. This is not the only example of Neolithic builders transporting blocks some distance for their monuments. At the Giant's Ring near Belfast at Ballynahatty in Co. Down, the blocks used to form the portal tomb there, although now heavily covered in lichen, are almost certainly from around Scrabo Hill, near Newtownards, Co. Down. The nearest source of dolerite to the Giant's Ring is about 10 km away. Did the Neolithic builders quarry the rocks there and then transport it to the site? Were blocks of rock available nearer the site having been dropped by the ice. It is impossible to prove. But dolerite was the deliberate choice of rock for Ballynahatty, however it was moved.

The prominent single stone outside the circle, at about 2.5 m high, is markedly different in texture and composition to the blocks making up the rest of the circle. It has a distinctly igneous texture and, unlike the metamorphic rocks of the circle, it is coarse-grained, consisting of a white mineral and a dark green mineral in roughly equal proportions.

The rocks in the immediate area around the stone circle are quartzites, quartz schists and marbles or limestones. There are no igneous rocks in the near vicinity, so the presence of the igneous-textured outside stone is very unusual.

So why did the Neolithic people use two distinctly different rock types in the construction of the stone circle and the standing stone outside the circle? One possibility is differences in colour and reflectivity. Since these stone circles have been exposed to the ravages of the atmosphere for thousands of years, they are often deeply weathered and covered in lichens, their colour often obscured. However, the two rock types at Beltany, when freshly erected, would have had very different appearances and reflectivity. The uprights of the circle, made of quartz and mica schists, are light coloured, often a golden-brown shade that would have reflected sunshine brightly. By contrast the igneous rock of the solitary upright outside the circle would have appeared darker. This solitary upright is likely to have been sourced at Croaghan Hill, some 5 km away from the site, and would have had the colour and reflectivity of the dark green mineral, hornblende.

Another noticeable feature of the location of the Beltany Stone Circle is the commanding view of the surrounding countryside that can be enjoyed. The circle is set inside a surrounding ring of low hills that are a distance of up to 6 km away and, sitting on a low knoll, the stones are set within this wider saucer-like structure in the overall landscape. In other words, the ring of stones is a small-scale representation of the larger-scale landscape. From the centre of the ring the variable heights of the uprights also mirror the topography of the surrounding hills.

Landscape with a higher purpose

The processes and motivations of monument building are complex. Often we can do little more than wonder at the meaning of these 'Earth features' and marvel at what we have been left with. But what is clear is that all of the

Neolithic monuments and monument-building activity were attempts either to modify the landscape for everyday domestic purposes or else to manufacture a ritual landscape in which the underlying geological features were special or sacred and needed modifying to enhance their cultural importance.

Some megaliths were designed to modify and alter the shape of the landscape and to be at odds with it. Others had the opposite aim, to fit in with existing landscape features. The selection of rock types also appears to have been from the nearby bedrock at times, while at other times blocks from considerable distances away were chosen, as if the desire was to include the monument in whatever was considered to be the complete geographical unit at the time.

The Neolithic people viewed, interacted with and altered their landscape at many levels including at the mundane,

MYTHOLOGY AND GEOLOGY

The curse of the dwarf

The Slaghtaverty dolmen, near Glenullin in Co. Londonderry, is the reputed burial site of an infamous dwarf who terrorised local people and enchanted women with his magical powers and the music he played on his harp. It is said the chieftain Cathan finally killed him but that he returned the next day from his grave demanding a bowl of blood. He was killed once again, this time by a sword of yew-wood, and re-buried upside down to ensure he would never walk the Earth again. However the ground was poisoned at the spot and the whole series of events became known as the time of '*dreach fhola*'. In Irish this means 'bad blood' but English speakers pronounce it 'drac - oula'. The historian Patrick Weston Joyce recounted this tale in a book published in 1880. It is believed that Bram Stoker, who wrote the novel *Dracula* read the historian's work some 17 years before he published his famous work. The area around the Slaghtaverty dolmen is still considered unlucky or cursed. As recently as 1997 workmen attempting to clear a tree found their brand new chainsaw stopped without reason on three occasions. Furthermore, when an attempt was made to lift a great stone here, a steel chain suddenly snapped cutting off the hand of a worker and allowing blood to seep into the soil. Local folk will advise you to avoid disturbing or even photographing the place in case you offend the one who still lies there.

The stones of the Beltany Stone Circle, Co. Donegal, set in the wider circle of the surrounding hills

everyday level of extracting material for tool-making and construction purposes, but also for higher-level functions involving the sacred and ceremonial aspects of their culture.

The building of monuments creates an entirely new sense of time and place around the landscape. Instead of allowing only the natural topography to create the sense of place, monument building is a way of establishing or enhancing the significance of locations. Once that has happened, those locations become part of the consciousness of the people who live and work around them until their perception of the landscape as a whole is changed. There is a new relationship forged between the people, their landscape and time, with perhaps a new and greater awareness of their existence in the landscape as part of the continuum of time that includes ancestors as well as future generations.

The desire of the people of the Neolithic age to make considerable modifications to the parts of the landscape thought of as special or sacred reveals a marked change in attitudes to nature, in comparison to the Mesolithic predecessors who lived on the island for thousands of years without making any such changes.

Since megalithic monuments were clearly designed to last a very long time there is a recognition of the concepts of time past (the significance and memory of ancestors) and time future (represented by the enduring place of the monument in the landscape).

Megaliths often remained significant long after their original purpose was lost and the people who built it had disappeared. Many examples exist of later cultures adopting the monuments from an earlier society. For instance, there is substantial archaeological evidence of Bronze or Iron Age people using Neolithic monuments. Many of these special sites continued to be special from the beginning of the Christian era and often into the present day. In other words, the meaning and significance of the monument may change without its form changing.

A case in point is Scrabo Hill in Co. Down, which has the remains of Iron Age hut circles near the summit. But it also has a Gothic tower, added in the nineteenth century to commemorate the Third Marquis of Londonderry. In the twenty-first century it is the location each Easter Sunday morning of a Christian service at sunrise. All of these activities have made use of a place in the landscape considered special.

So the landscape underpinned all activities of the Neolithic people in a way that 7,000 years later we may have difficulty appreciating. But in this age the landscape became defined as a relationship between people and the places they inhabit. Landscape served a higher purpose. It became much more than a mere inherited geological construction modified by the forces of weathering and erosion. Indeed the landscape became a physical form exerting a powerful influence on the way people lived.

DID YOU KNOW?

The megalith builders used the resources of the landscape very well, building a relationship between themselves and the places they inhabited. At the Knocknarea peninsula, Co. Sligo, for example, they circled around the land according to the season. Kitchen middens found on the north shore of Ballysadare Bay consist of banks of oyster and mussel shells up to 100 m long and 5 m deep. These were the base camps for the Neolithic people who built the monuments at Carrowmore and Knocknarea. Their house sites on higher ground were probably used for summer grazing.

Meanwhile, at Glencloy, near Carnlough, Co. Antrim, there is evidence of exploitation of flint resources at sea level, while the main settlement sites were set back from the coast in the valleys, with possible summer grazing sites on the higher ground. In both cases the impression is gained of a people using all of the components of landscape and its resources, not just for survival but for the industrial, social and cultural needs of the population.

View southwards over Ballysadare Bay, Co. Sligo, from Knocknarea

St Patrick's Well, Holywell, Co. Fermanagh

DID YOU KNOW?

Irish society has always had a relationship with the water arising out of the physical landscape in the shape of wells and springs. These were frequently depicted as coming from the otherworld, considered sacred or holy, or able to bestow some sort of power or healing on those who drank or bathed in them. The so-called holy wells were most often visited during the four great festivals of the Celtic calendar – Imbolc on 1 February (the coming of spring), Bealtaine on 1 May (the coming of summer), Lughnasa on 1 August (the start of autumn) and Samhain on 1 November (the start of winter). With the coming of Christianity the role of holy wells and springs did not diminish, instead they were adopted into the new religion, many becoming associated with a particular saint. One example is St Patrick's Well in the aptly named Holywell just outside Belcoo in Co. Fermanagh. Here, where limestone meets sandstone, water reaches the surface and flows outwards in two directions from the well. The waters are reputed to be the coldest in Ireland and are said to cure nervous and paralytic disorders as well as stomach ailments. Although now associated with St Patrick, this is an ancient Lughnasa site that even today is a place of pilgrimage between Bilberry Sunday (the last Sunday in July) and the 15 August. Known as St Patrick's Tub, it is believed St Patrick himself blessed the well during his travels around the country.

The west door, Grey Abbey, Co. Down

THE ERA OF BUILDINGS

The remaining prehistoric period in Ireland, dominated by the discovery of metal, saw the addition of an array of new constructions and buildings placed amid and alongside the Neolithic megaliths and tombs on the landscape.

The Irish Iron Age is also called 'The Dark Age' because so little is known about it. Where and how people lived is still vague. Records are so far confined to the discovery of defensive hillforts and linear earthworks, while evidence of settlements on the island consists largely of hearths and pits and other remains that have returned radiocarbon dates for the Iron Age.

The spread of iron technology is bound up with interactions with the Celts, who gradually brought their distinct culture from Europe. It included chariot burials,

> **" It was during my enchanted days of travel that the idea came to me, which through the years, has come into my thoughts again and again and always happily – the idea that geology is the music of the earth. "**
>
> **Hans Cloos**
> **Prominent German geologist, early twentieth century**

fortified hilltop construction, and the art-style known as La Tène. So the Iron Age in Ireland was also the age of the Celts, and they soon came to dominate. Writings about this pagan society in heroic tales such as *An Táin Bó Cúailnge* (*The Cattle Raid of Cooley*) and others in the Ulster Cycle, one of the four great cycles of Irish mythology, record and heavily embellish the Celtic way of life.

The effect on the landscape of the combined efforts of the Bronze and Iron Age peoples was a significant contribution to Ireland's fascinating and mysterious archaeological narrative.

Celtic constructions

The Iron Age saw the emergence of dozens of small kingdoms in Ireland. The Celtic warrior culture had brought the need to hold and consolidate territory and to defend it by building hill fortifications and linear earthworks into the landscape.

The majority of the 60 or so hillforts uncovered so far in Ireland are in the south and south-west of the island, but there are a number of prime examples in the north, including a type of hillfort defence structure known as inland promontory forts.

These Celtic constructions made special use of places where the topography or geological conditions combined to form a spur or neck of land with steep or sheer cliffs on three sides. This allowed the closure of the remaining fourth side with

An aerial view of the promontory fort on Lurigethan, Glenariff, Co. Antrim, shows the parallel lines of the earthworks used to protect the inland side of the fort (on the right of the picture)

a defensive rampart of some form. For example, the northern side of the valley at Glenariff is formed of the promontory Lurigethan and an aerial view of it shows clearly the line of the earthwork built on its fourth side.

Earthworks

Earthwork-building also shaped the archaeological landscape and two examples of note dating from the Iron Age are the Dorsey and Emain Macha (Navan Fort), both in Co. Armagh.

The Dorsey dates from the early Iron Age and appears to be linked with the site at Emain Macha, the ancient royal capital of the Kings of Ulster. The Dorsey consists of the remains of two, roughly parallel, massive earthen bank and ditch ramparts over 1.6 km long that lie outside an ancient route to Emain

Macha. The name Dorsey comes from the Irish '*doirse*', meaning doors, or gates, and refers to the passes through the earthworks. It is thought the Dorsey was built to protect travellers on their way to Emain Macha.

Emain Macha is a huge circular earthwork enclosing about 5 hectares on the summit of a drumlin, commanding extensive views. Technically this is not a fort and archaeologists believe that it once housed a great wooden structure and was more likely to have been used as a complex for rituals, probably with royal or aristocratic connections. It is one of a small number of sites celebrated as ancient royal or provincial capitals. The others being Tara, Co. Meath (Meath, the 'middle' province), Knockaulin, Co. Kildare (Leinster) and Cruachan, Co. Roscommon (Connacht).

The Dorsey earthworks, Co. Armagh, can be seen as a double hedge in the lower part of this aerial picture

Navan Fort, Co. Armagh – the close proximity of a now flooded limestone quarry can be seen

MYTHOLOGY AND GEOLOGY

Carlingford Lough – the Cooley Mountains are on the right and the Mourne Mountains to the left

The Cattle Raid of Cooley

It is hardly surprising that the volcanic landscape of south Ulster, where the borders of the provinces continually shifted, was the setting for the quintessentially Celtic tale of cattle raiding, jealousy and the role of women. *An Táin Bó Cuailgne – The Cattle Raid of Cooley* is one of the most outstanding stories of Irish mythology. Bulls were prized like nothing else in Celtic society so when Queen Maeve of Connacht heard there was a brown bull in Ulster, at Cooley, that was prized more than the white bull belonging to her husband and King of Connacht, Ailill, she then raised an army to steal it away. She was jealous because the brown bull had proven to be phenomenally fertile. It had been born into Maeve's herd, but the brown bull moved into Ailill's herd rather than be owned by a woman. Maeve was determined not to be outdone by her husband and after the collapse of a deal that would have given her the brown bull of Cooley on loan for one year, she raised an army against Ulster, determined to capture it and bring it back to Connacht. In earlier times, the goddess Macha had placed a curse on the men of Ulster after the king had forced her to race against a chariot while heavily pregnant. The curse meant that the men of Ulster would become like women in labour at the hour of Ulster's greatest need. So as the army of Connacht approached the Gap of Ulster between Slieve Gullion and the Cooley Mountains, the men fell under Macha's spell. Only Cúchulainn was immune. He stood alone against Maeve and the armies of Connacht until the spell was lifted and the armies defeated, though not before Maeve managed to steal away the bull and bring it back to Connacht where it fought and killed Ailill's white bull. But the brown bull himself was mortally wounded, and eventually made his way back to Cooley before dying of exhaustion.

Ringforts and cashels

After the Iron Age, Ireland underwent a number of radical changes, including an increase in pasture and arable farming and the introduction of Christianity early in the fifth century. This was the next great phase of landscape modification in Ireland.

Among the results of the changes was the construction of tens of thousands of ringforts, small circular enclosures some 30 m in diameter, usually consisting of an earthen bank and then an outer fosse or ditch. The bank consisted of the material dug out from the ditch.

The banks around ringforts mark the perimeter of farmyards, not fortresses, and would have enclosed houses and farm buildings. In areas of shallow soil the builders constructed banks of stone and these stone enclosures are known as cashels. One of the finest examples of cashel-building on the island is Grianan of Aileach in Co. Donegal, the seat of the Kingdom of Aileach and an important centre of culture and power from 800 BC to 1200 AD. It is probably best described as an early medieval cashel within an earlier ring fort. It consists of a large stone-built wall inside a number of earthen banks. The massive stone wall is almost 4 m thick and encloses an area of over 23 m in diameter. As with megaliths, stone structures appear eternal and immovable, so this cashel was probably built as a visual symbol of the landscape its ruler could survey and master from its dominant position within the landscape.

MYTHOLOGY AND GEOLOGY

Who was Macha?

Emain Macha is just a few kilometres west of Armagh City. From the Irish, the name means 'the twins of Macha'. Armagh itself comes from Ard Macha meaning 'the heights of Macha', for the city is of course built on drumlins. But who was Macha? Macha was a woman from the otherworld who, heavily pregnant, was forced through the boasts of husband Crunnchu to race King Conchobhar's horses in a chariot race at the grand assembly of Ulstermen. Her husband had bragged that his wife could win any race, angering the king, who was proud that his horses were the finest in the land. The king forced her to race despite her condition. The race was tight and as Macha crossed the finishing line, ahead of the king's horses, she collapsed. As she lay dying Macha gave birth to twins and ever since the place of the king's assembly became known as Emain Macha or 'the twins of Macha'. With her dying breath Macha cursed the king and the men of Ulster by saying that for nine generations to come, in the hour of their greatest need, the men of Ulster would be crippled by the pains of childbirth, a curse that would come true in *The Cattle Raid of Cooley*.

The cathedrals of Armagh at dusk

The Grianan of Aileach cashel, Co. Donegal, was the seat of power of the Kingdom of Aileach from 800 BC to medieval times

DID YOU KNOW?

Devenish monastic site, Co. Fermanagh

The round towers of Ireland show the admirable skill and delicate perception of gracefulness of outline possessed by the Iron Age Irish builders. The earliest of them were constructed with rough stonework, but the latest were built with finely dressed blocks, using lime mortar. In the celebrated Devenish Round Tower on the monastic site at Devenish Island, within the Marble Arch Caves Global Geopark in Co. Fermanagh, a hard blue local limestone was used in the construction of the west door, contrasting with a softer brownish sandstone used earlier in one of the churches on the island.

Cloisters, crosses and castles

The Christian era brought the first stirrings of a recorded history in Ireland. It heralded social changes such as the development of literacy and books via the medium of Latin, and witnessed a developing architecture of churches and cemeteries.

Nendrum Monastery, Strangford Lough, Co. Down, was part of the early Christian church in Ulster from around the seventh century

In 431 Pope Celestine I sent Palladius, the first Irish bishop, "to the Irish believing in Christ". These early Christians had been converted by missionaries from Britain at or near the end of its existence as a province of Rome. St Patrick certainly came to Ireland from this background, brought, perhaps along with thousands of others, as a slave.

The first Irish churches were established in a similar way to the churches in Britain and mainland Europe, with small communities governed by a bishop, local to that community. But by the sixth century a system of monastic communities had developed, ruled not by a bishop but by an abbot. At this time monastic life became popular in Ireland and was often associated with patronage from royalty and other people of stature in the community.

The legacy of the period to the local landscape is a series of carved stone crosses and pillars, shrines, stone churches, abbeys and round towers. These needles in the skyline introduced the first real stone architecture and use of mortar in Ireland.

The ruins of two abbeys on opposite shores of Strangford Lough in Co. Down show the contrasting types of monastic settlement from the early Christian period in Ireland. Nendrum Abbey on the west side of Strangford Lough was part of the early Christian church in Ulster and probably developed as a monastery around the seventh century.

It consists of three stone enclosures; the inner one contained the church and graveyard and the middle one had round houses for the monks to live in. Nendrum had craft workshops in its outer precincts and it would have been a monastic town of considerable size. As well as practising agriculture the monastic community built fish traps in the nearby lough and also constructed an elaborate tidal mill made of slabs of the local sandstone and using millstones identified as Mourne granite. The remains of the church and round tower show that the building material used was entirely of the local blue-grey sandstone, with no elaboration or decoration.

In contrast to what was probably a bustling community at Nendrum, on the opposite side of Strangford Lough, was the settlement at Grey Abbey, founded in 1193 by the Cistercians, a contemplative religious order. The ordered layout of Cistercian buildings, generally around a square or quadrangle, contrasts sharply with the more informal arrangements of the earlier Celtic monasteries. Grey Abbey has an elaborately carved west door, with locally-derived Scrabo sandstone used in the carving. The other parts of the building are constructed of a mixture of Scrabo sandstone, principally as corner stones, grey sandstone similar

DID YOU KNOW?

St Patrick's Church of Ireland Cathedral, Armagh

St Patrick's Roman Catholic Cathedral, Armagh

Armagh has been the ecclesiastical capital of Ireland since the fifth century AD, when St Patrick founded his church there. Today there are two cathedrals, both named after him. An early nineteenth-century remodelling of an original built in the late thirteenth century, St Patrick's Church of Ireland Cathedral consists of large blocks of iron-rich sandstone. Its plinth and tower are constructed from a coarse-grained rock known as conglomerate, which contains large angular blocks of Carboniferous limestone. Meanwhile, St Patrick's Roman Catholic Cathedral, designed in the French Gothic Revival style and built in 1840, consists largely of grey Carboniferous limestone, cut locally at Ballybrannon Quarry.

Grey Abbey, Strangford Lough, Co. Down, founded by the Cistercians in the twelfth century

Bonamargy Friary, Ballycastle, Co. Antrim

Unlike the later high crosses, the carvings on the standing stone at Glencolumbkille, Co. Donegal, did not change the outline shape of the stone

The Kilnasaggart Pillar Stone, Co. Armagh, is probably the earliest example of stone carving in the Christian period in Ireland – its inscription records the dedication of the site by a man who died early in the eighth century

to that used at Nendrum, and some boulders of igneous rocks, mostly Scrabo dolerite. The range of rock types used can be still clearly seen. The pale brown Scrabo sandstone and the brownish Scrabo dolerite show much greater signs of weathering than the much fresher blue-grey sandstone.

Elsewhere, examination of the material used in the building of Bonamargy Abbey, near Ballycastle in Co. Antrim, suggests that the builders used local Carboniferous sandstone, similar to that exposed along the foreshore to the east of the town. The abbey's walls and carved windows and doors still retain a pale, buff-coloured sandstone which was soft enough to be easily carved and dressed for use as a building stone. The ruin still retains much of a finely carved east window.

High crosses

Of all the monuments so commonly dotted about the countryside, the high crosses are among the most evocative and representative of Ireland. The crosses that survive in Ireland and to a lesser extent in Britain represent virtually the only carved free-standing monuments of the early early medieval period in western Europe. The cross at Carndonagh, Co. Donegal, appears to be the first of these free-standing high crosses so suggestive of the 'Land of Saints and Scholars'.

They were carved at a time when there were few opportunities to produce monumental work, other than that commissioned by the Christian church. Earlier prehistoric monuments and pillars inscribed with crosses such as seen at Glencolumbcille in Co. Donegal

DID YOU KNOW?

Carrickfergus Castle, Co. Antrim

Generally dominant on the landscape, the surrounding geology is an important factor in a castle's ability as a stronghold. Carrickfergus Castle was built on what geologists call an igneous intrusion, a dyke, that formed as part of the nearby Antrim lavas. The harder, more resistant dolerite forming the dyke means that it stands above the softer mudstones of the surrounding area and improves its defensive position. Geological maps of the Carrickfergus area show that the dyke runs inland in a north-westerly direction for several hundred metres.

Ardboe Cross, Co. Tyrone, a fine example of a high cross, was erected around the tenth century and displays a range of biblical scenes on all its sides

did not change the shape of the stone and carving was generally restricted to markings on the surface. These carved standing stones are generally made of schist with the soft mineral, mica, running through it. This type of rock lends itself to carving with relatively shallow cuts. The outline of the stone is not modified, unlike the later 3-D carved sandstone crosses, for example.

The crosses tend to be aligned east–west and consist of a base, a shaft, a stone ring around the intersection, and a capstone. Some taller shafts are in segments. The earliest ringed crosses had abstract decoration, passing through a transitional stage before Biblical scenes were introduced on the faces.

This led to later forms, the Scripture Crosses, characterised by carvings on all four sides. These carvings often show scenes from the Old and New Testaments with the Last Judgement on one side of the cross head, and the Crucifixion on the other. The stone most commonly used was sandstone, although granite was used in Leinster and limestone was common in certain areas of the west of Ireland, including Co. Clare.

High crosses were erected around monastic sites, mainly to illustrate stories from the Bible, but also perhaps as status symbols. They were probably important sites in the ceremonial calendar of the religious community.

Castles

Dunluce Castle on the north Antrim coast is a superb example of a late medieval fortification. Built by the MacDonnells on a site previously occupied by the MacQuillan clan, it had a magnificent manor house with a great hall and splendid bay windows within the fortress walls.

The castle was easily defended because it was sited on a promontory of strong basalt with the entrance at the narrow landward side. But it could not defend itself from an unfortunate accident when its seaward end containing the kitchen fell into the waves one night in 1639, killing several servants.

The frames of the bay windows and the corner stones are made from buff-coloured sandstone, most likely Carboniferous in age and sourced from the area around Ballycastle to the east. The remainder of the castle is constructed of basalt blocks, some of

Dunluce Castle, Co. Antrim, is sited on a basalt headland for defensive purposes and contained within its walls a splendid manor house with a great hall

The distinctive yellow rock used on the corners of Carrickfergus Castle, Co. Antrim, was quarried at Cultra, Co. Down, across Belfast Lough

which show the characteristic hexagonal shape of the basalts at the Giant's Causeway.

A feature of the conquest of Ireland by the Normans was the construction of great stone-built fortresses or castles in the period from the end of the twelfth century to around the beginning of the fourteenth. The best examples of these structures are on the eastern side of the island and one of the most spectacular is at Carrickfergus in Co. Antrim.

For an undertaking of such a large scale the availability of suitable building material is crucial. Carrickfergus, on the north side of Belfast Lough, was ideally situated in close proximity to abundant supplies of durable basalt from the Antrim Plateau, blocks of which were used to build the bulk of the castle by the Normans in the twelfth century. In addition to basalt they used a rare and distinctive light yellow-coloured and magnesium-rich limestone called dolomite for the decorative corner stones. This was drawn from across Belfast Lough at Cultra, Co. Down.

From traditional cottages to landmark structures

Ballymote Castle in Co. Sligo, a 'keepless' castle, was the last of the Norman structures to mark the northern landscape and by the early decades of the seventeenth century the Ulster Plantation had brought about large stone structures such as Derry's Walls and defended houses such as Parke's Castle in Co. Leitrim, or Ballygalley Castle, now a hotel on the Co. Antrim coast. The age of medieval defences was being

DID YOU KNOW?

With its spectacular location perched on the basalt cliffs overlooking Downhill Strand and Lough Foyle, the Mussenden Temple in Co. Londonderry is one of the most iconic buildings in Northern Ireland. The foundation of the building, originally designed as a library and built in 1785 for the Earl of Bristol, Bishop of Derry, is local basalt, while the curved walls and 16 columns are of Carboniferous sandstone, sourced from Ballycastle.

Mussenden Temple, Downhill, Co. Londonderry

Parke's Castle, Co. Leitrim, was built by one of the planters in Ulster early in the seventeenth century

replaced by structures for gracious living, though self-protection was still very much in the minds of the builders.

The way of life of a building's occupants, and the way they use their shelters, is of great influence on the form of their buildings. The size of the family, how food is prepared and eaten, the way people interact, and many other cultural considerations all affect the layout and size of dwellings.

Buildings concerned with the ordinary rather than the monumental structures of a country are described as vernacular architecture. But there are no architects' drawings: vernacular architecture involves local traditions, knowledge and craftsmanship handed down and modified from generation to generation.

Up until recent times the rural buildings in Ireland had a distinctive style. Of course, once seen all over the country, the vernacular architecture of the traditionally thatched, lime washed cottage, with a curl of smoke rising from a turf fire, is one of the picture-postcard images of the island. Stone-built of necessity because of the lack of timber, they reflected the locally available materials, the damp Irish climate and local traditions.

In many areas in the north and west of Ireland, a bed outshot – a kind of extension or alcove in a traditional cottage – is a feature of this strand of vernacular architecture. The outshot provided extra space without the need to alter the roof height or find additional timber. The outshot usually housed a bed next to the kitchen hearth for the oldest

A derelict cottage with bed outshot, the Sperrins, Co. Tyrone

inhabitants of the dwelling. A shallow outshot meant that much of the bed protruded into the kitchen floor area but many were deep enough to house the whole bed.

Because infertile soils did not readily support large trees, bed outshots are probably due to the absence of suitable timber for long rafters. This is a fine example of geology's impact on our ancestors, and just one of the geological influences on building styles throughout Ireland. There are often recognisable building style differences between the generally less prosperous rugged north and west and the richer lowlands of the east and south.

From the creamy Co. Fermanagh limestone farmsteads, to the rugged basalt ladder farms of the Antrim Glens,

and the sturdy granite cottages of the Mournes in Co. Down, there was a vibrant vernacular architecture in the north of Ireland until the end of the nineteenth century. But in the twentieth century it began to be replaced with housing that owed nothing to the local norms. As a consequence of commercial and industrial farming, increasing urbanisation and suburbanisation, and the rise in popularity of prefabricated house building methods, traditional regional styles declined heavily.

Towards modern landmark constructions

The great manor houses of the Plantation of Ulster and the fine residences of post-Plantation Ireland's aristocracy and landed gentry added further markers to the landscape. Remnants from this

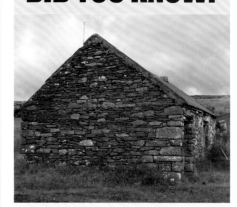

The gable wall shows the cottage is made of metamorphic and sandstone rocks sourced from the local landscape

Estyn Evans, in his classic study *Irish Folk Ways*, has pointed out that outshots (*cailleach* in Irish, derived from *cúil theach* 'the back of the house') are generally confined to the north of a line that runs from Cushendun in Co. Antrim to south-western Galway.

This distribution coincides with the location of the oldest rocks in the country, the ancient granites and metamorphic rocks – schists, gneisses and quartzites – that are so characteristic of much of the north and west of the country.

The example above in the Sperrins is built of a mixture of schists and coarse sedimentary rocks from the surrounding area. These rocks produce generally poor soils and consequently trees are scarce.

DID YOU KNOW?

The Albert Clock, Belfast

The precarious lean of the Albert Clock was due to the rise in sea level about 8,000 years ago when Belfast Lough covered much of what is now downtown Belfast. This sea deposited the infamous 'Belfast sleech', a thick, dark, foul-smelling marine mud, containing fossils such as oysters, mussels and snails. The material has major implications for any building project in Belfast city centre because it has very poor weight-bearing capabilities. Anything built on it usually has to be heavily strengthened. Weak foundations in the sleech and rotten wooden piles were the cause of the lean in the Albert Clock.

Florencecourt, Co. Fermanagh, an eighteenth-century house, former home of the Earl of Enniskillen

Derry's Walls are built from metamorphic rock from quarries in the nearby Sperrin Mountains

period, often situated in superb positions in the landscape, include Monea Castle and Florencecourt in Co. Fermanagh as well as Mount Stewart, Co. Down, and Lough Rynn House, Co. Leitrim.

The construction of Derry's Walls is considered to be one of the first major pieces of urban planning on the island. Londonderry is now the only remaining completely walled city in Ireland and is one of the finest examples of city wall structures in Europe. Derry's Walls vary in width from 4 to 12 m, forming a walkway some 1.5 km long. They are constructed largely of a metamorphic rock, schist, from the Sperrin Mountains in the now disused quarries at Prehen and Kittybane.

One of the earliest recorded uses of the sandstone found in Scrabo, Co. Down, was as coffin lids during Norman times. But its real importance was as a building stone in the late-nineteenth century, and many of the most prominent and impressive buildings of Belfast were constructed from it. One the best known examples is the Albert Clock in High Street, Belfast, which has recently undergone extensive structural work to stabilise a tilt that was beginning to rival that of the more famous Leaning Tower at Pisa. Another is the Robinson and Cleaver building in central Belfast, built in 1888 with stone from quarries in Newtownards.

This six-storey former linen warehouse was a prestigious department store in Belfast city centre for many years. Towards the end of the nineteenth century the use of Scrabo sandstone began to decline in favour of darker

The Robinson and Cleaver building in central Belfast, built in 1888 with Scrabo sandstone from the quarries near Newtownards

DID YOU KNOW?

One of the key features of the Mourne Mountains' landscape is the dry stone wall that runs for more than 30 km over the main peaks of the eastern Mournes. Constructed to define the boundaries of the water catchment area for the Silent Valley Reservoir, which supplies Greater Belfast, the Mourne Wall crosses 15 summits of the mountain range. The Belfast Water Commissioners built the wall as an unemployment relief scheme in the early part of the twentieth century. The granite wall in itself celebrates the crafts and techniques of the stone masons of the Mournes, skills that continue to this day, but it is also a twentieth-century attempt to make a mark on the landscape. To that end the Belfast Water Commissioners were in line with the dolmen builders and stone circle erectors who inhabited this area several thousand years ago and who also altered the landscape and left their mark on it.

The Belfast Water Commissioners' Boundary Wall, Mourne Mountains, Co. Down

The Guildhall, Londonderry, is built from a mixture of local sandstone from near Dungiven, Co. Londonderry, with the detail carved from imported Scottish sandstone

coloured sandstones, often imported from Scotland.

Derry's Guildhall, originally built in 1887 and destroyed by fire in 1908 before being rebuilt in 1912, dominates the city skyline and is another significant northern structure. Built in a Tudoresque Gothic style, the main stonework is local Carboniferous sandstone from near Dungiven, Co. Londonderry, while the tracery and carved detail is in red sandstone of Permian-Triassic age, probably from Corsehill in Scotland. This use was in line with many of the prominent buildings being constructed around the same time in Belfast where the use of imported stone was fashionable.

Other celebrated constructions on the northern landscape include Parliament Buildings at Stormont, completed in 1932 and fronted with Portland stone, a limestone from Jurassic times quarried on the Isle of Portland in Dorset. Portland stone has been used extensively throughout Britain, notably in important public buildings in London such as St Paul's Cathedral and Buckingham Palace.

In the centuries before the building of the houses that we live in today, the Irish countryside became dotted with thousands of structures made of the earth, wood and bedrock dug, hewn and quarried mainly from their local surroundings. The era of buildings has left a wide selection of major landmarks, significant constructions and important edifices adorning the northern landscape. Whether used for defence, governance, worship, trade or just everyday living, these structures have left us with a rich series of monuments and landmarks and a built heritage that has continuously developed the landscape from prehistoric to modern times.

Parliament Buildings, Belfast

Like Parliament Buildings at Stormont and landmark buildings in London, the City Hall, Belfast, is built with Portland stone, the building stone of choice at the end of the nineteenth century when the city council wished to celebrate the prosperity and prestige of the city

Typical drumlin country in south Co. Down

ANCIENT RESOURCES, MODERN DILEMMAS

Since the earliest of times society has used local resources and in the process created large-scale changes to the landscape, the environment and lifestyles in the north of Ireland. We have seen that in Neolithic times the use of better axes allowed the more efficient clearance of woodland, speeding the expansion of agriculture, with all its implications for changes in the environment and way of life for all later residents of Ireland. In the same vein, the use of crushed basalt as road stone to build a new motorway, or the employment of concrete drainage pipes to drain marshy areas, causes significant impacts on our modern landscape.

Rocks and mineral resources taken from the landscape over time met specific needs, provided tools, weapons and monuments, and were put to use in a range of buildings from cottages to castles. The requirements of modern lifestyles also need meeting, but they demand a far greater breadth, depth and pace of resource extraction from the ever-evolving landscape. A contemporary transport network, for example, calls for vast quantities of sand and crushed stone. All of it must come from quarries or sand pits. Yet both the removal of materials from the land and their use to construct new roads create highly visible impacts on the landscape.

The earliest inhabitants of the island used a wide range of rock types and minerals and showed a remarkable aptitude for selecting the right material for what they needed. For example, they used granite when a hard, durable rock was required for millstones. We now know that millstones from the tidal mill at Nendrum on the shores of Strangford Lough came from the Mournes, about 50 km away from the site. Similarly, our ancestors crushed and ground grain using hand mills known as querns, and for these a coarse, resistant rock was required. Many quernstones formed from hard gritstone have been found throughout counties Down, Armagh and Monaghan. These are the same rocks the modern quarrying industry in Northern Ireland now uses extensively as a road stone and as an aggregate for concrete.

With the arrival of contemporary advanced industrial farming, Ireland's transformation to an almost entirely 'derived' or 'cultural landscape' was complete. The coming of the Industrial Revolution in the mid-nineteenth century provided the impetus for the modern phase of change that impacted on the northern landscapes. What is interesting is that the industrialists of the nineteenth century and the early Irish settlers had a common understanding. In their own way both groups understood minerals and rocks, what geological resources actually are and how they could use them.

Mining and quarrying

Chalk, which is a variety of limestone, is an example of the way our recent forebears used a natural resource industrially. In nineteenth-century Co. Antrim farmers spread lime over their fields because it reduced acidity and improved the soil's capacity for growing cereals. To make the chalk usable it had to be heated in limekilns, generally using fires powered by coal or peat, and these kilns became a common feature across the northern countryside. Burnt chalk, or lime, was also the main ingredient in lime mortar, which throughout the nineteenth

> ## " What cannot be grown must be mined or quarried. "
>
> **Anon**

The Giant's Head, White Rocks, Portrush, Co. Antrim

DID YOU KNOW?

Antrim chalk is composed of the billions of skeletons of micro-organisms known as coccoliths that lived in a sea that covered most of Ireland and northern Europe some 75 million years ago. The skeletons, made of the mineral calcite, fell to the sea-bed and formed the thick and distinctive deposit of white limestone known as chalk. It can still be seen over much of northern Europe, including the famous White Cliffs of Dover in England. Coccoliths are only about 5–10 microns in diameter, that is, 5–10 millionths of a metre. When finely powdered Antrim chalk's purity means that it is highly useful as a filler and inactive ingredient in medicines, and it is commonly used in tablets such as aspirin.

A ruined lime kiln in the Marble Arch Caves Global Geopark, Co. Cavan

Murlough Bay, Co. Antrim – it is difficult to imagine that this idyllic rural scene was a major industrial site in the late eighteenth and early nineteenth centuries, with a number of coal mines and lime kilns in operation

century became the preferred jointing material for masonry walls. When the burnt lime was mixed with water and a colouring pigment it then became lime wash or 'whitewash' and used to cover the walls of buildings.

Abandoned chalk quarries still surround Carnlough, a small coastal town and port on the east Antrim coast. A narrow-gauge railway brought the material from the quarries to the harbour via a distinctive limestone bridge across Carnlough's main streets. The harbour is also constructed from limestone. Much of the limestone was exported to markets on the west coast of Scotland and to England, where it was used as a flux in the iron smelting industry. Changes in agricultural practices mean that there is now little demand for lime for spreading on fields, but the limestone quarries at nearby Glenarm still produce finely crushed and ground limestone for a whole range of uses such as filler in pills and tablets or in toothpaste.

Coal-mining

The principal coal deposits in Britain occur in rocks of Carboniferous age (about 310 million years old); however rocks in Ireland of this age are predominantly limestone. But there are still places where coal-bearing rocks occur, including Coalisland and the coastal strip from Ballycastle to Murlough Bay, Co. Antrim.

The town of Ballycastle is a notable draw for tourists in the area today, but in the late eighteenth and early nineteenth centuries its natural resources made it a hotbed for industrial activity such as coal-mining, glass production, soap manufacture, salt production and iron-

DID YOU KNOW?

The Antrim Coast Road

Powdered Antrim chalk is the principal component in much of the road marking material used in Britain and Europe. Much harder than most of the equivalent deposits in England, it is very white and durable. This means it holds its colour and is good at resisting wear and tear from the passage of traffic over the lines.

Carnlough, Co. Antrim – the railway arch over the main street carried limestone from the chalk quarries that are still visible in the hills behind the town. Both the arch and the harbour wall are constructed from chalk

The entrance to the Gobb Colliery, Ballycastle, Co. Antrim, in the early part of the twentieth century

Alluvial gold grains panned from rivers in the Sperrin Mountains – these grains are less than 1 mm in size

Because of its geology Northern Ireland is probably the most likely area in Great Britain and Ireland to have precious metal deposits. Perhaps surprisingly, gold is a reasonably widespread natural resource in Ireland as a whole. It occurs from the extreme south in Wexford, Galway in the west, around Dublin and the Wicklow Mountains in the east and importantly for the north, in Donegal, the Sperrins, the Mournes and Antrim.

The gold used to manufacture ornaments in the Bronze Age could have come from what are called placer deposits, found in the form of flakes or nuggets of gold in the sands and gravels of streams and rivers. Using gold-panning techniques it is still possible to extract gold today from rivers around the Mournes, Sperrins or around Cushendun in Co. Antrim.

Gold occurs as what is known as 'native gold' which means it is already in the form of metal and unlike other metal ores such as copper, requires no smelting. This means it either can be melted before being poured into a mould, or it can be hammered into shapes such as ribbons or flat gold leaf.

The modern production of gold in Ireland is very different. At the Curraghinalt and Cavanacaw gold deposits in Co. Tyrone the gold is dispersed through the bedrock in veins of quartz. Due to the hardness of the quartz veins and the depth at which the gold occurs, the ore must be mined.

smelting. Much of the industrial activity was due to one man, Hugh Boyd. When he eventually died in 1765 many of the industries he had established declined and vanished. However, his glassworks in particular had used coal from the local area and coal-mining carried on intermittently there until the late twentieth century.

Coal has also been mined from other locations in the north of Ireland going back to the seventeenth century. Arigna, located in north Roscommon close to the borders of both Sligo and Leitrim, has a 400-year coal-producing tradition that only ended in 1990 with the closure of its mines.

Iron ore and bauxite

In the middle of the nineteenth century bright red laterite, best seen at the Giant's

Causeway, was another local resource our recent forebears learned to exploit, this time as a source of iron ore. A place where the laterite was predominant was Slieve Nanee, to the north of Glenravel, Co. Antrim. Slieve Nanee is derived from the Irish and means Iron Mountain, which suggests a long-standing awareness of the potential of the laterite as a resource. Since the iron ore was smelted in Britain, railway lines were constructed to haul it to the sea at Red Bay, Co. Antrim, for export.

The laterite beds were also a source of an aluminium ore called bauxite, and mining of the beds continued after the decline in iron ore mining at the end of the nineteenth century. By the 1930s the last of these bauxite mines had closed, but not before almost 300,000 tonnes of aluminium ore had been extracted (equivalent to 60,000 tonnes

The view from inside an old iron ore mine in the Glenravel–Newtowncrommelin area, Co. Antrim

DID YOU KNOW?

The Thomas Thompson Memorial Fountain at the intersection of Ormeau Avenue and Bedford Street in Belfast underlines how important a clean water supply was to the growing population of the city in the second half of the nineteenth century

A rock known as the Sherwood Sandstone underlies most of the Belfast area and the Lagan Valley. The rock has the ability of allowing the sandstone to act as an aquifer; that is, the sandstone is porous and the spaces between individual sand grains can therefore fill with water. This property made the Sherwood Sandstone an important source of drinking water in the late nineteenth-century Belfast area. In the days before a properly regulated public water supply, these sandstones were the basis of a world famous bottled water industry that used artesian wells drilled down into the sandstone beds underneath Belfast. An artesian well allows the water that has travelled through porous rock to rise to the surface. Firms such as Ross, Cantrell & Cochrane and Grattan supplied drinking water from carts to houses in the city. They also supplied aerated water, cordials and other soft drinks and sold to a world-wide market until the outbreak of the First World War when the demand dropped. At Ross's premises just off Cornmarket in central Belfast, there was a deep artesian well inside the building. Ross's advertising pamphlets used what is known as a bore-hole log to show the depth their water was coming from and to emphasise how pure their source was. The bore-hole was almost 160 m deep.

McGladdery's Brickyard, Springfield Road, Belfast, in the early part of the twentieth century

A modern brickworks in Co. Tyrone

Underground crushing and screening plant in the Kilroot Salt Mine, Carrickfergus, Co. Antrim

Salt is essential for human life and so has long been important to industry. The seas that evaporated in the hot desert environment of east Antrim 230 million years ago are responsible for leaving behind thick deposits of salt. Seams of salt have been discovered along the Antrim Coast over the past century and more, accounting for the salt mining activity around Carrickfergus since the 1960s. Many people would be surprised to learn that travelling on the main road from Carrickfergus to Whitehead entails driving over extensive mine workings. However there is cause to be grateful to the Carrickfergus mine for the salt supplied for road gritting during periods of frost and snow during the winter. Many of the early salt mines were unregulated and with the passage of time it is not always clear where the old underground workings existed. A disused salt mine near Carrickfergus collapsed in the 1990s, forming a deep crater at the surface, with all the obvious implications for the safety and well-being of the people living nearby. This illustrates the need for careful regulation of the methods used in underground mining in residential areas.

of aluminium metal). But for World War II creating a demand for aluminium for aircraft production, this might have been the end of the mining story in Co. Antrim. However, between 1941 and 1945, a further 300,000 tonnes of ore was mined, as much as had been extracted in the previous existence of the mines.

Brick-making

The Industrial Revolution in the northern part of Ireland meant a massive expansion in the population of Belfast, as people left the rural areas to seek work in the growing industries in and around the city. These people had to be housed, and so street after street of terrace houses

were built, as well as the familiar mills, warehouses and foundries and other industrial buildings. Associated with this expansion there was also an equivalent rise in the number of schools, churches and administration buildings. The expansion of the city constituted one of the greatest landscape alterations ever

seen in Ireland, and even within living memory it is possible for residents of the city to remember former green areas that succumbed to 'urban spread'.

Most of the new building was in brick, and by the middle of the nineteenth century there were over 30 brickworks in

Belfast alone. But like many industries in the area, brick-making began to decline after World War I and had ceased entirely in the Belfast area by the early 1970s. Nowadays the only brick manufacturing in Northern Ireland is in Co. Tyrone.

Rocks and roads

Until recent times the removal of rock from the landscape was on a relatively modest scale. Few examples of the quarry workings of earlier times now remain on the landscape because vegetation has since covered them and erosion has rounded any steep faces. Our modern infrastructures and constructions, however – the road and rail networks, the structures that provide a water supply for the population, the ports, airports, houses and homes – demand rocks in quantities undreamed of even at the beginning of the twentieth century. As a result of satisfying this demand the quarrying industry has become one of the biggest modifiers of our landscape since the Ice Age.

Removing large quantities of rock from the ground serves a number of purposes.

A modern sandstone quarry in Co. Down

The Antrim Coast Road, south of the town of Glenarm

In the northern part of Ireland the main purpose is road stone. The crushed rocks are usually mixed with some form of bitumen or tar to form tarmac. They can also be used as an aggregate, which is mixed with cement to form concrete or concrete products such as building blocks or drainage pipes. Northern Ireland is fortunate in having a range of hard rocks suitable for use in industry. The Antrim basalts, and the sandstones making up much of Co. Down and Co. Armagh, provide crushed rock for the local construction industry. Some of the Co. Down sandstones are high-quality and exportable for use as motorway road stones in Britain and mainland Europe. In fact, the M25 motorway around London contains a great deal of sandstone originating in Co. Down.

The ability to travel by road across the whole of Ireland is actually a fairly recent phenomenon; even into the early part of the twentieth century some areas of the country were still almost inaccessible by wheeled transport. In the past, road-building was highly labour-intensive and the road-making materials were often just taken from adjacent fields or temporary quarries nearby. The impact on the landscape would have been minimal, although the social impact of a new road was usually much greater.

In contrast, the four-lane motorways of today make large and often controversial impacts on the surrounding countryside. The average width of a motorway is almost 30 m, not counting the land on either side, compared with the figure of around 16 m set for new mail coach

DID YOU KNOW?

The mineral gypsum has been mined from the rocks of Co. Cavan for over 70 years. The construction and building plaster industries use gypsum extensively and it is also used to make Plaster of Paris. Transforming gypsum into plaster is one of the oldest processes known to man. Crushed and heated in kilns, the gypsum is ground down to obtain a powder.

Plaster is a particularly environmentally-friendly material, requiring little energy for its manufacture as well as being non-toxic and recyclable. The extraordinary Crystal Cave of Giants at the Naica Mine in Chihuahua, Mexico, is known for its 12 metre-long selenite crystals (selenite is a form of gypsum).

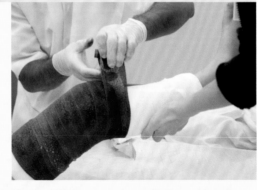
Plaster of Paris, commonly used in the making of casts, is made from the mineral gypsum, which is mined at Kingscourt, Co. Cavan

roads at the end of the eighteenth century. Although often efficiently and quickly built, modern roads still have to take account of and negotiate the underlying geology of their route. The building of the Antrim Coast Road, one of Ireland's most scenic driving routes, illustrates the problems caused when demands for road expansions come up against age-old geological weaknesses.

The population of the Glens of Antrim in north-east Ireland used to be poorly served by land transport, leaving communities remote and isolated. Efforts in the 1830s to improve the situation began with an engineer named William Bald, who designed a road along the Antrim Coast that would open up the Glens to the rest of the country, allowing access from the south to villages like Glenarm and Carnlough.

The problem with the construction of the road then, and which has continued to plague the road ever since, is that a very weak and unstable clay lies under the high cliffs of chalk and basalt along the Antrim Coast leading to instability causing frequent rock falls. Because the clay is very soft it may squeeze out from below the chalk and basalt cliff rather like toothpaste from a tube, forming mudflows like that at Minnis, near Glenarm, Co. Antrim.

Engineers have constructed retaining walls along the route to prevent mudflows blocking the road. However, since it is constantly on the move the mud continually needs to be trucked away. The instability of the clay also weakens the structure of the cliffs above, and there is a constant risk

of rocks falling down onto the road. Following two serious rock falls in the late 1960s it was decided to try to solve the problem by moving the road seawards, away from the danger zone at the base of the cliff.

This required the construction of a new causeway to hold a completely new section of road, out from the base of the cliff and over what had previously been the sea floor. A line of chalk blocks runs along the seaward side of the construction to protect it from wave action. A low wall signifies the top of a line of piles designed to anchor the road to solid bedrock.

While William Bald's road can be hailed as a brilliant piece of civil engineering for its time, even the best modern techniques can do no more than keep the mudflows and rock falls at bay. Road closures still happen in the area and motorists travelling on the Antrim Coast Road still need to keep careful lookout as they wind their way through the beautiful scenery.

Road making in Co. Donegal around 1900 was in sharp contrast to the process of road building nowadays. The process was fairly labour intensive and materials for the road and walls were taken directly from the surrounding area

A modern motorway network showing the amount of land taken up by the main carriageway and the various roundabouts and slip roads

DID YOU KNOW?

As of 2010, various companies have taken out licences to explore for minerals and gas resources in over 65% of Northern Ireland's land area. One company is mining gold and it appears likely that another will be seeking planning permission to do the same. Parts of Northern Ireland also hold out the prospect for gas. New technology has made it more likely that the known locations of gas may prove commercially viable in the future.

An exploration drilling rig, Co. Tyrone

Twenty-first-century geology

The vibrant cultural heritage alive in Ireland in the twenty-first century celebrates not just a past and abiding understanding of the landscape, but also our ancestors' great ability to find the best ways to exploit water, rocks, minerals and the other opportunities their surroundings provided. As we have seen, seeking out and using the Earth's natural resources has been, and today remains, completely fundamental to the development of civilisations all over the world.

Over the millennia, humans have found natural resources through their powers of observation. Lives depended on knowing local environments, and this made our ancestors much more familiar with the land supporting their needs than would be the case for most citizens in the north of Ireland today. So if a farmer observed a mineral in a rock glinting in the sunlight 500 years ago, he would be drawn to it. Probably he would dig it out. Perhaps he would put it to cosmetic or industrial use. It would be unlikely that he would leave it be, and in this sense farmers were among the first prospectors or exploration geologists in Ireland.

Of course, some individuals are better than others at assessing areas and hunting out natural resources. People with a prospector's 'Midas touch' were highly regarded in early society because their skills represented an opportunity for land owners and entrepreneurs to create jobs and wealth. John Caldwell Bloomfield, for instance, founded the now world-famous Co. Fermanagh-based Belleek Pottery in 1858 after he noticed and became intrigued by what he saw as the unusual sparkling of the limestone that coated the thatch-roofed cottages of his estate. He ordered a geological survey of his land. It revealed the necessary raw materials to make pottery – feldspar, kaolin, flint, clay and shale – and a new industry was born.

To the natural ability of observation, early geologists added the skills of scientific measurement and interpretation. It was the fundamentals of observation, measurement and interpretation that led to the recognition of different types of rocks on Earth and an understanding of how they formed. In turn, this helped establish the longevity of geological time and the foundations of how geologists use evidence about the structure of the planet to discover natural resources. So in many ways geology is the original forensic science. Essentially geologists confront a series of three-dimensional landforms, a time frame, and evidence from the past written in the rocks. They then try to construct a 'whatdunnit'.

> **❝ all honour to the pickaxe and its modern equivalents; they are still the most important intermediaries in the millennial dialogue between the elements and man ❞**
>
> **Primo Levi,
> The Periodic Table, 'Carbon'**

DID YOU KNOW?

As more of our population becomes urban-based, the need for geologists to increase their understanding and explain the subsurface in areas of high population density becomes progressively more important. For instance the Belfast Metropolitan Area occupies 7% of the land area of Northern Ireland, yet one third of our population lives there. The first geological need in an urban area like this is to understand the available water resources and to ensure that any pollution entering the natural groundwater system is minimised. There is also a requirement to ensure that ground

Geologists interacting with geological models in a 3-D environment

stability information is available to allow engineers, architects and developers to plan and use appropriate construction methods to ensure safe buildings. There is also a need to identify areas that may have past land use problems and to eliminate any industrial contamination that may pose human health threats. To address these needs the GSNI is building 3D computer models of the rocks below Belfast and Londonderry. Using information from thousands of bore-holes it is becoming possible to view our cities from below and to determine environmental, geological and engineering conditions to support planning and development.

This can be difficult when the rocks are hidden. Over 99% of the rocks in the northern part of Ireland are not on view; they are covered by soil, sand, gravel and peat. Only through the skills of the geologist, which date back here to the seventeenth century, have we been able to build up a picture of the local rock resources and aid the exploration and identification of where our natural resources might lie. Previous mining ventures have left a legacy of over 2,000 mine workings in Northern Ireland. These have produced a wide range of commodities and raw materials including salt, coal, iron, aluminium and lead.

Current mines in Northern Ireland produce gold and salt.

Today, Northern Ireland's geologists continue to explore what lies under our rocks and hard places and what makes the landscape of the northern portion of the island unique. Aided by modern techniques and technology, local geology is contributing vital data, knowledge and solutions to an ever-increasing range of twenty-first-century issues and problems.

The primary actor in this work is a body within the Department of Enterprise, Trade and Investment, the Geological

The different lines and colour intensities on this magnetic map allow geologists to make interpretations of rocks up to several kilometres deep in the Earth

Castle Espie Wetlands Centre, Co. Down, a former quarry and now a modern eco-friendly tourist attraction

Understanding how planet Earth came into being and how it works has been the domain of geologists for centuries. But in the past 30 years the science of geology has become ever more central to an increasing range of issues. Now, because of their expert knowledge of the natural processes that give rise to environmental problems, today's geologists have a leadership role in a range of areas that affect society, including the sustainable development of natural resources. Twenty-first-century geology promotes environmental responsibility and sustainable development, stewardship of the mineral resource sector and effective planning when it comes to exploring, developing and using mineral resources.

Survey of Northern Ireland (GSNI). The GSNI has brought international recognition and a clutch of industry awards to Northern Ireland geology through its Tellus Project, a remarkable survey of the entire local landscape.

The Tellus Project is the most concentrated geological mapping venture ever undertaken in Northern Ireland. It involved work on the ground and an airborne survey that saw an aircraft flying over the whole region at a height of just 56 m along parallel lines only 200 m apart. The plane collected highly specialised magnetic, electrical conductivity and gamma-radiation data. The capture of this high-quality information has made the 14,000 sq km of Northern Ireland one of the most

geologically surveyed parts of the globe. Given that the geology of the area is one of the most varied compared to any similar sized spot on planet Earth, the new data heavily enhances Northern Ireland's international reputation within the science of geology.

The results from the Tellus Project have provided valuable new insights into Northern Ireland's landscape and have led to the production of specialist maps that greatly extend and deepen our knowledge of the geology, soils, natural resources and the local environment. Among the uses the information is being put to is verifying and therefore increasing the confidence of previously held data, supporting exploration for mineral and hydrocarbon resources,

helping with land-use planning, managing the environment and addressing climate change. The data is also helping society to deal with the risks caused by natural hazards such as landslides, radon gas and ground instability, and supporting renewable energy, urbanisation, marine science and landscape tourism. The improved mapping has also prompted renewed interest in mineral prospecting and has led to increased enquiries and requests for prospecting permits for precious and base metals.

Use it or lose it

The Tellus Project was intended to address two fundamental issues: firstly, to increase the understanding of Northern Ireland's natural resources base; secondly, to collect 'baseline'

As the Tellus survey aircraft crosses over Co. Down, coils on its wing-tips map changes in the magnetic field and electrical conductivity of the Earth beneath

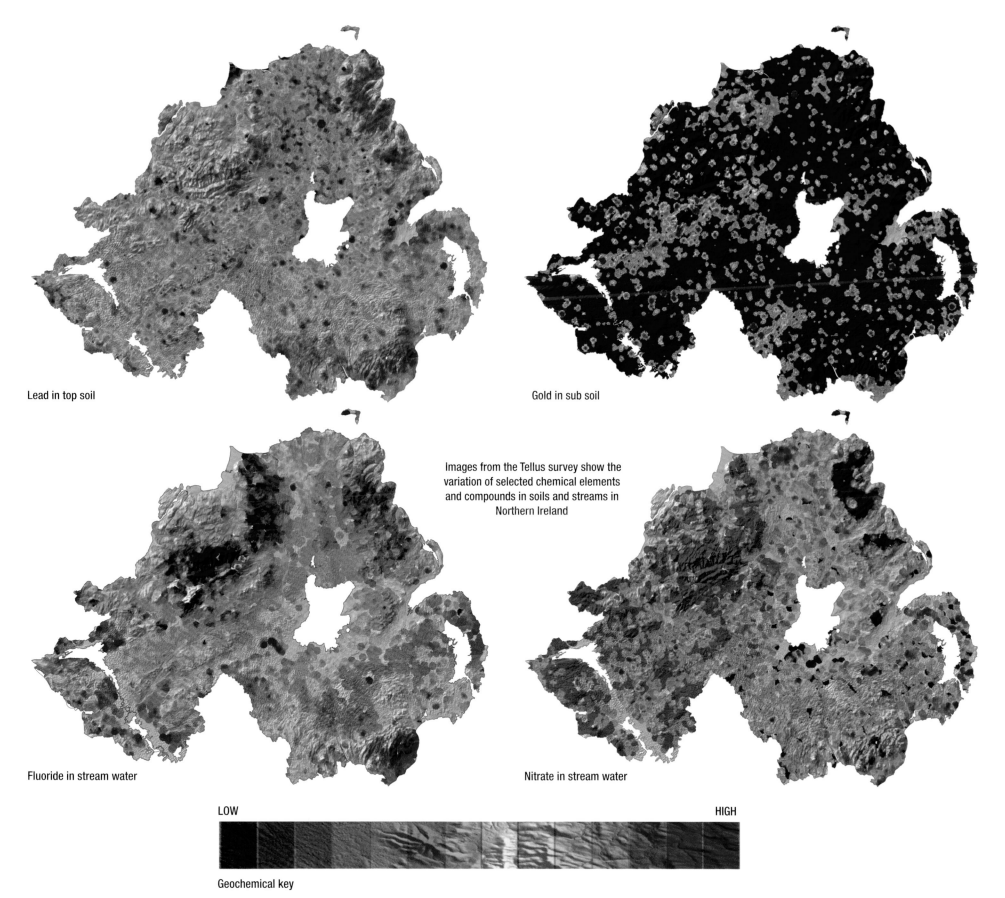

Lead in top soil

Gold in sub soil

Images from the Tellus survey show the variation of selected chemical elements and compounds in soils and streams in Northern Ireland

Fluoride in stream water

Nitrate in stream water

LOW

HIGH

Geochemical key

data about the environment. As with many geological datasets, the use of the information throws up a perennial two-sided predicament. On one side is the need to identify and use our natural resources, on the other is the need to manage and protect our environment.

For example, until 1985, the historically valuable site at Emain Macha in Co. Armagh was threatened by the expansion of a nearby limestone quarry. When the location of transport routes or the need to extract natural resources threatens important sites like this – as also happened to the archaeological complex at the Hill of Tara in Co. Meath – the demands of modern society creates controversy and cultural clashes over the need to preserve history and the need for society to progress.

The Tellus Project survey crew review the proposed flight path over Northern Ireland before take-off

DID YOU KNOW?

If something cannot be grown, then it has to be dug out of the ground. Quarry products are essential for developing a society as they are quite literally the building blocks of modern civilisation. As a result of its varied geology, Northern Ireland has a diverse aggregates base and the construction industry – accounting

Quarrying and mining works are essential to modern civilisation

for about 12% of the economy – has developed around it. Aggregate includes sands, gravels and the crushed rock used in the local manufacture of cement, concrete products and road surfacing materials. Production of these primary construction materials will continue for the foreseeable future. Did you know:
- A new house requires about 50 tonnes of aggregates?
- About 14 tonnes of aggregates are needed per head of the population per year?
- A typical family indirectly needs three lorry loads of aggregate every year?
- Northern Ireland requires around 24 million tonnes of aggregates each year?

On one hand we demand better roads, improved housing, a reliable water supply, efficient disposal of sewage and other waste. At the same time the cost of these services in terms of the amount of natural resources used to supply them is something that as a society we often baulk at.

As a society we have important choices to make. If we maximise the use of our local natural resources, we can provide employment and manage the extraction processes to a high environmental standard. If we minimise the use of our local resources we will import our commodities from elsewhere, probably not create as many local jobs and perhaps have to accept that an overseas mine or quarry may not operate to the same environmental standards that we would expect at home. Which scenario leaves us

DID YOU KNOW?

In the field the main tools of the geologist were once paper, pencils and rock hammers, now they use the latest mobile technology

Unless we deny the development of the human species the need for newly mined mineral resources is going to continue. In fact, it is estimated that five times the amount of metal that has been mined in the world to date will be needed just to keep up with projected expansion of the human population in the next 50 years. But is exploring for mineral resources and mining them good or bad? Consider these facts in making up your mind:
- We need minerals to live.
- Mineral extraction disturbs only about 0.1% of the Earth's land surface.
- Exploration for natural mineral resources is essentially non-invasive.
- The extractive industries are relatively short-lived and transient compared to billions of years of geological time (see page 17).
- Employment in rural areas.

better off? What are our moral obligations? Another issue with natural resources is that 'they are where they are'. In other words you cannot move a quarry or mine somewhere else because the location of the natural resource is fixed. It is usually a straight choice between use it or lose it. But if we choose to use our natural resources will we not scar, blight and damage the landscape? This is one of the most difficult environmental questions in the twenty-first century.

There is much that can 'scar' a landscape – an 'inappropriate building', a new road, a sand or gravel pit – and the public perception of a blight on the landscape can vary. What is unusual about buildings and roads is that over time they tend to gain acceptance. However, people frequently view a quarry as unacceptable, probably because they do not make the link between the rock from the quarry and its use in the construction of the road or building. But quarry products are essential ingredients of life in the twenty-first century. Everyone uses them, and everyone benefits. They literally help us to make more of life.

Differing uses of the same landscape on the southern edge of the Antrim Plateau show how we deal with the issue of resources and the environment. Quarrying over the last 50 years has extensively altered the appearance of Black Mountain and White Mountain, two of the hills that fringe Belfast to the west. Having been bought by the National Trust, the adjacent Divis Mountain, in sharp contrast, is now being used as a recreation area, a so-called green lung for the city that offers stunning views over Belfast Lough and the hills of Co. Down.

Divis Mountain, a recreational area looking over the city of Belfast and Belfast Lough

White Mountain, just to the west of Divis Mountain in Belfast, is clearly affected by extensive quarrying operations, as is Black Mountain in the background of the picture

Modern-day modifications to the landscape in the Sperrins near Dungiven, Co. Londonderry

DID YOU KNOW?

Minerals closely associated with rubies and sapphire deposits were found in the 1990s near Malin Head in Co. Donegal's Inishowen peninsula. There were hyped up suggestions that Donegal could have become Ireland's answer to Kimberley – the 'city that sparkles' and centre of the South African diamond-mining industry. The suggestion created a stir among Donegal residents, some with hopes of a new prosperity, and others with fears of environmental damage to an unspoilt region with significant tourism potential. In the end the diamond prospecting was not a great success. But the local population would have faced major dilemmas had it been otherwise.

The Brookeborough Diamond, discovered in the Colebrook River in Co. Fermanagh in 1816, is the only diamond ever found in Ireland. But its origins and authenticity are surrounded by mystery.

Malin Head, Co. Donegal

There is no doubt which of the two uses of the landscape is the more attractive, but the reality is that a society needs both. We need the resource taken out from the ground, but we also need to be able to avail ourselves of the aesthetic value of a walk in the open air over the high ground of the plateau.

Much can be now be done to lessen the effects of essential quarrying and mining – careful management, landscaping and screening during the workings, for example. And environmental legislation now requires quarry and mine companies to restore the landscape after their commercial operations are finished. Even without planned rehabilitation, nature has a way of disguising the earlier ravages of mines and quarries. Vegetation has recolonised the lead mines at Conlig and the sandstone quarries on Scrabo Hill, Co. Down, decades after their commercial life ended, the sharp edges of exposed rock now softened by ravages of the weather. With careful management by the government these quarries have been transformed into nature reserves for birds like the peregrine falcon and made into country parks for walkers and cyclists.

All of this of course involves extra expense. The question is, are we willing as a society to pay the price and make the sacrifices necessary to stop our landscape from being compromised? The use it or lose it choice and the question of what blights the landscape are thorny and recurrent; they will remain until society works out how to supply new and bigger houses and new and better roads without tapping into the sources of the raw materials. The challenge we all face is to integrate our lifestyles and working lives with the landscape and environment we inherit and inhabit.

As we have every period of geological time represented in the environment surrounding us in Northern Ireland it is unsurprising that our portion of planet Earth is so diverse and spectacular. Millions of years of erosion and relatively recent glaciations have helped design the rich tapestry of our local scenery and lush landscape. Every county has its own unique beauty and we are justifiably proud of the local landscape, which is our natural inheritance. We also have as our heritage a fascinating range of historical stone monuments, great buildings and mighty structures with one thing in common – they all came out of the ground.

DID YOU KNOW?

Remains of the lead mine works at Conlig, Co. Down. For a brief period in the late nineteenth century Conlig was one of the biggest producers of lead ore in Europe

The base metals of copper, lead and zinc underpin today's technologically driven society. Transport systems rely on these metals for the production of cars, aeroplanes and ships and the communications industry would never have reached its current level without the use of these metals in telephones, televisions, computers, satellites and cables. Areas of Co. Londonderry, Co. Tyrone and Co. Fermanagh have the highest possibility for base metal deposits in Northern Ireland.

Thanks to geology, today and long into the future, the people of Ireland's northern landscapes will continue to inhabit, appreciate and capitalise on the diversity of our ever changing natural landscape.

ROCKS AND MINERALS OF THE NORTH

This book mentions over 30 different types of rock and minerals relevant to the geology of the northern portion of Ireland. Here is a brief guide to them in plain English.

Rocks

Almost all rocks are composed of one or more minerals. Minerals are the 'ingredients' of rocks in the same way a fruit cake has components like currants or cherries held together by the cake mix.

Every mineral has its own unique chemical and crystal structure. Although many rocks contain visible crystals of individual minerals, a rock itself does not have an overall crystal structure.

Geologists use the types and the proportions of minerals present in rocks and the size of the mineral grains to classify rocks and name them. There are thousands of rock types. But they all fall into one of three main categories: igneous, sedimentary and metamorphic.

Igneous rocks

Igneous rocks are basically formed from cooled molten rock, or magma, from the Earth's interior. 'Igneous' comes from the Latin word for 'of fire'.

If magma spills onto the surface as lava then the rock it forms is called 'extrusive' igneous rock. If the magma cooled into rock underground and never made it to the surface, then it is called an 'intrusive' igneous rock.

Granite is the commonest intrusive rock in Ireland and basalt is the commonest extrusive rock. Dolerite and gabbro are intrusive rocks with the same composition as basalt, but because they cooled more slowly the mineral grains are coarser and more easily seen with the naked eye.

Examples of local igneous rock

Gabbro

Granite

Sedimentary rocks

Over time, weathering agents such as rain and wind break down rocks exposed above ground. Most sedimentary rocks are composed of the fragments and particles of broken-down rocks that accumulate, often in layers, after the wind, rivers or sea currents move the pieces around. Mudstones and sandstones, for example, commonly form this way.

The red sandstone formed in a desert environment, with shallow rivers and sand dunes. In contrast the grey sandstone formed on the bed of an ocean.

Rocks such as limestone and chalk come from the accumulation of animal remains like oysters or corals. Coal, which is also a sedimentary rock, comes from dead plant remains that accumulated in stagnant water where the processes of normal decay were greatly delayed.

Examples of local sedimentary rock

Desert sandstone

Mudstone

Conglomerate

Limestone

Marine sandstone

Metamorphic rocks

Metamorphic rocks are rocks that get changed, or 'metamorphosed,' into a new or different rock by the addition of heat or pressure or both. This can happen when a rock comes into contact with hot magma or lava. When heated or highly pressurised, such as during continental collisions (see page 14), metamorphic rocks such as slate, schist and gneiss are formed.

Extreme heat and pressure on rocks can also fracture them (faulting in geological terminology) and distort them into complex shapes (known as folding). Extreme pressure or heat changes (geologists would say 'metamorphoses') sandstone into quartzite, limestone into marble, and mudstone into slate.

Examples of local metamorphic rock

Gneiss

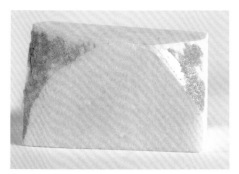

Marble

Quartzite

Schist

Slate

Minerals

A mineral is any natural, inorganic material formed by geological processes in the Earth. Different combinations of just a few chemical ingredients make up most minerals.

All minerals belong to a chemical group and various crystal structure groups. Each type of mineral has its own special properties that help to identify them.

Minerals are economically important. We mine them because of the need for a valuable element they contain or a certain property they may have. Others are mined for their beauty and rareness.

Examples of local minerals

Calcite

Flint

Gold

Mica

Quartz

MAPPING THE WAY

Geological maps are invaluable in understanding the northern landscape. They show up the differences in geological features and the variation in the rocks that lie beneath our feet. The maps use different colours for each rock or each group of similar rock types of the same age.

The pale blue colour in the map represents the limestones of the Fermanagh–Sligo region. The purple colour around Antrim shows the basalts of the Antrim Plateau. The pale pink colour is the area underlain by the metamorphic rocks of Donegal, which occur also in the Sperrin Mountains and around Torr Head on the east Antrim coast.

By mapping the different rock types, geologists can determine the relationships between rock formations. They can use this information to find, protect and safely extract mineral resources. They can advise where to build houses and roads (and where not to build them), and help society with stewarding the landscape and countryside through informed agricultural, construction and environmental practices.

Geological maps can reveal that if you live in parts of Co. Londonderry the material that lies under the foundations of your house belongs to the same group of rocks that make up the Sperrin Mountains to the south-east and the Donegal Highlands to the north-west. If you live in Omagh, you are close to the Omagh Thrust, a major break in the Earth's crust. It has moved many times throughout geological time and may be active again sometime in the future.

Regular users of the M1 motorway between Belfast and Dungannon might like to know they are driving over 250-million-year-old red sandstones. These rocks are 'aquifers' (they are able to hold and release water) and once helped provide the domestic water supply for the city of Belfast. At the south-west end of the Antrim Plateau the M1 crosses large deposits of clays. Clay is common around large parts of Lough Neagh.

A winter scene at the Gortin Lakes, Co. Tyrone, themselves a remnant of the Ice Age

Simplified bedrock

1. Metamorphic rocks: 1800 million years old
2. Metamorphic rocks: 600 million years old
3. Andesite lava and volcanic ash: 420–470 million years old
4. Basalt lava: 60–62 million years old
5. Greywacke, shale, sandstone and conglomerate: 440–480 million years old
6. Intrusive igneous rocks (excluding granites): 56–62 million years old
7. Intrusive igneous rocks (including granites): 56–62 million years old
8. Intrusive igneous rocks: 420–600 million years old
9. Intrusive igneous rocks: (mostly granites): 420–470 million years old
10. Lavas: 420–470 million years old
11. Limestone reefs: 330 million years old
12. Limestone and conglomerate: 330 million years old
13. Limestone, mudstone and sandstone: 350 million years old

14. Limestones and mudstones: 330 million years old
15. Limestones and shales: 350 million years old
16. Metamorphic rock quartzite: 600 million years old
17. Mixed sedimentary rocks: 251–299 million years old
18. Mudstone: 430–440 million years old
19. Mudstone and limestones: 185–199 million years old
20. Mudstones and limestones: 420–600 million years old
21. Mudstones and sandstones: 330 million years old
22. Mudstones, greywacke and conglomerate: 430–440 million years old
23. Rhyolite lava: 60 million years old
24. Rhyolite lava and volcanic ash: 420–470 million years old
25. Sands, clays and lignites: 23 million years old
26. Sandstone conglomerate and mudstone: 330 million years old

27. Sandstone, conglomerate: 350–390 million years old
28. Sandstone, mudstone and conglomerate: 345–350 million years old
29. Sandstone, mudstone and salt: 216–251 million years old
30. Schist and marble: 420–600 million years old
31. Sedimentary rocks: 320–360 million years old
32. Sedimentary rocks including coal: 320–330 million years old
33. Sedimentary rocks including chalk: 80 million years old
34. Volcanic rocks: 330 million years old
35. Volcanic rocks: 420–470 million years old
36. Volcanic rocks: 56–62 million years old
37. Volcanic rocks: 600 million years old
38. Weathered basalt: 60–62 million years old

Geologists can also use satellite imagery, aerial photography and terrain models to understand and explore the landscape. The map opposite shows changes in the relief of the land and also features formed by the action of ice. The higher ground of the Donegal Highlands in the west, for example, standing in sharp contrast to the low ground of the Lough Neagh Basin or the fertile farmland of Co. Down and Co. Armagh. The higher ground of the Sperrins, the Antrim Plateau and the Mournes in south Down are also prominent features. Geologists use images like these to point up the contrasts and highlight the geological differences and features of the landforms and how they fit into the complex evolution of the island of Ireland.

Geological maps also highlight the considerable range in the age of the rocks underlying the spectacular scenery in the northern portion of Ireland. We have relatively recent layers of peat only a few thousand years old, and rocks that have been around for over 1,000 million years. This variety is the result of a complex geological history involving the formation of rocks in a diverse set of conditions that included tropical oceans, hot deserts, active volcanoes and barren, Arctic-like wasteland.

The River Bann, cutting across the volcanic landscape of Antrim, was once a major highway for the early inhabitants of Ireland

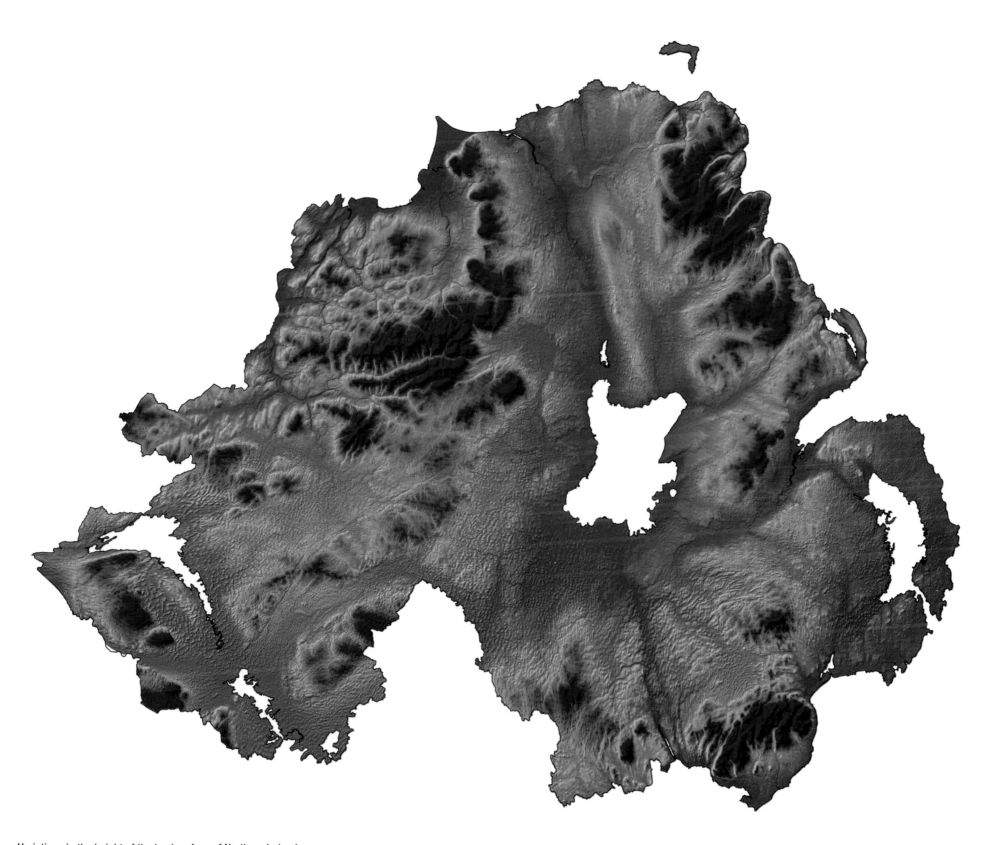

Variations in the height of the land surface of Northern Ireland

FURTHER INFORMATION

This publication provides an introduction to the geological basis of our landscape to people who may have little or no experience of matters geological. For readers who have had their appetites whetted, there is a wide range of other books and materials available.

General

The Geological Survey of Northern Ireland (GSNI) provides geological maps, guides, pamphlets and other services and material. In the Republic of Ireland the Geological Survey of Ireland (GSI) does the same.

Geological Survey of Northern Ireland
Colby House
Stranmillis Court
Belfast BT9 5BF
Tel: +44(0)28 9038 8462
Email: gsni@detini.gov.uk
Web: www.bgs.ac.uk/gsni

Maps

For those interested in geological maps the 1:250,000 scale geological map for Northern Ireland provides detailed coverage of Northern Ireland, plus Co. Donegal and parts of counties Sligo, Leitrim, Cavan, Monaghan and Louth in the Republic of Ireland.

For those wishing to explore the geology of the whole island the 1:500,000 map will provide the relevant information. In addition, maps recently published by GSNI showing the geology of popular tourist areas such as the Giant's Causeway and Ballycastle include explanatory text and photographs for the general reader. A full list of maps published is available from GSNI.

Guide books

The best way to experience geology is on foot. There are a number of guide books and walking guides that explain the geology of the northern landscapes of Ireland and provide detailed instructions of where you can examine the geological evidence for yourself and thus draw your own conclusions. Titles include 'Walk the Sperrins', 'Walk Cuilcagh' and 'Walk South Ulster'. These guides are all available from GSNI and GSI.

Guide books include: *A Story through Time,* by Patrick McKeever, and *Classic Geology in Europe 5 The North of Ireland,* by Paul Lyle.

Books

The Geology of Northern Ireland: Our Natural Foundation, published by GSNI, edited by W.I. Mitchell, provides a detailed account of the geology of Northern Ireland shown on the 1:250,000 map. While it is primarily written with geologists and other geoscientists in mind, there is much to interest walkers, climbers, naturalists and others engaged in outdoor pursuits.

One of the best studies of the Irish landscape, including details of the Ice Age and the changes to the landscape since the retreat of the ice and the arrival of the earliest settlers, is *Reading the Irish Landscape,* by F. Mitchell and M. Ryan. It provides a comprehensive account of the flora and fauna of Ireland as it emerged from its frozen state and catalogues the changes to the landscape, both natural and man-made in the roughly 13,000 years since the last ice cap melted.

The *Atlas of the Irish Rural Landscape,* edited by F.H.A. Aalen, K. Whelan and M. Stout, provides a wide-ranging description of all aspects of the Irish landscape. Details of the archaeology can be studied in the *Archaeology of Ulster: from colonization to plantation* by J.P. Mallory and T.E. McNeill.

Clubs and societies

If you are interested in meeting with like-minded enthusiasts, organisations such as the Belfast Geologists' Society and the Belfast Naturalists' Field Club are long-established groups that meet regularly. There are lectures covering all aspects of the landscape during the winter months and field trips and excursions throughout Ireland during the summer. Programme and contact details may be found on the Habitas website: www.habitas.org.uk.

Useful websites

- Geological Survey of Northern Ireland: www.bgs.ac.uk/gsni

- Geological Survey of Ireland: www.gsi.ie

- Ulster Museum: www.nmni.com/um www.habitas.org.uk

- Northern Ireland Environment Agency: www.ni-environment.gov.uk

- Environmental Protection Agency: www.epa.ie

INDEX

PHOTO CREDITS

Front cover, reverse front cover, reverse back cover Chris Hill

Page ii   Chris Hill

Page viii   Chris Hill

Page iv   Chris Hill

Page v   Harrison Photography

Page vi   Chris Hill

Page vii   Chris Hill

Page viii   Chris Hill

Page 1   Chris Hill

Page 2   TL Chris Hill
TR Chris Hill

Page 3   BL Chris Hill
TR Chris Hill

Page 4   TL Chris Hill
BC Chris Hill
TR Crown copyright

Page 5   BL Chris Hill
TR Chris Hill

Page 6   TL Chris Hill
BR Fermanagh District Council

Page 7   TL Chris Hill
TR Chris Hill

Page 8   TL Chris Hill
TR Chris Hill
BL Chris Hill

Page 9   TL Chris Hill
BL Crown copyright
TR Chris Hill

Page 10   TL Chris Hill
BR Chris Hill

Page 11   TL Cavan County Council
TC Chris Hill
TR Chris Hill

Page 12   Chris Hill

Page 13   TR Andy McInroy
BR iStockPhoto

Page 14   TL iStockPhoto
TC US Geological Survey
TR iStockPhoto

Page 15   TL US Geological Survey
BL Crown copyright

Page 16   Chris Hill

Page 17   iStockPhoto

Page 18   BL Natural Environment Research Council
TC Chris Hill
TR Paul Lyle

Page 19   TL Crown copyright
BL Chris Hill
TR Chris Hill
BR Chris Hill

Page 20   TL Fermanagh District Council
TR Natural Environment Research Council
BR Crown copyright

Page 21   TL Chris Hill
TR Institute of Earth Sciences, Iceland photographer, Halldór Olafsson

Page 22   Chris Hill

Page 23   BC Natural Environment Research Council

Page 24   Top Chris Hill
Middle iStockPhoto
Bottom National Museums Northern Ireland

Page 25   TL National Museums Northern Ireland
BL Natural Environment Research Council
TR Chris Hill

Page 26   Chris Hill

Page 27   TL Chris Hill
TR Chris Hill

Page 28   BL Chris Hill
TC Chris Hill
TR Institute of Earth Sciences, Iceland photographer Halldór Olafsson

Page 29   BL Chris Hill
TR Chris Hill

Page 30   TL Chris Hill
BR Chris Hill

Page 31   TC iStockPhoto
TR Chris Hill

Page 32   TL iStockPhoto
BL Chris Hill
TR Crown copyright

Page 33   Chris Hill

Page 34   Chris Hill

Page 35   Top Chris Hill
Middle Crown copyright

Page 36   TL Chris Hill
BR Chris Hill

Page 37   BL Chris Hill
TR Chris Hill

Page 38   Chris Hill

Page 39   TL National Museums Northern Ireland
TC Chris Hill
TR Chris Hill

Page 40   Chris Hill

Page 41   Chris Hill

Page 42   National Museums Northern Ireland

Page 43   TC Crown copyright
TR Chris Hill

Page 44   Crown copyright

Page 45   Chris Hill

Page 46   Chris Hill

Page 47   TL Chris Hill
           BL Provided by Northern
           Ireland Environment
           Agency, Crown copyright
           TR Provided by Northern
           Ireland Environment
           Agency, Crown copyright

Page 48   BL iStockPhoto
           TR National Museums
           Northern Ireland

Page 49   TL Courtesy of Marble Arch
           Caves Global Geopark
           TR Chris Hill

Page 50   TL Chris Hill
           TR Chris Hill

Page 51   Top Chris Hill
           Bottom Chris Hill

Page 52   Chris Hill

Page 53   Chris Hill

Page 54   TL Chris Hill
           TR Chris Hill

Page 55   TL Chris Hill
           BR Chris Hill

Page 56   Chris Hill

Page 57   Chris Hill

Page 58   Chris Hill

Page 59   BL Chris Hill
           TR Chris Hill
           BR Chris Hill

Page 60   TL Chris Hill
           TR Chris Hill

Page 61   Chris Hill

Page 62   Chris Hill

Page 63   Chris Hill

Page 64   Chris Hill

Page 65   Provided by Northern
           Ireland Environment
           Agency, Crown copyright

Page 66   TL Provided by Northern
           Ireland Environment
           Agency, Crown copyright
           BL Chris Hill
           TR Crown copyright

Page 67   TR Chris Hill
           BR Chris Hill

Page 68   TL Chris Hill
           TR Chris Hill

Page 69   TC Chris Hill
           TR Chris Hill
           BR Chris Hill

Page 70   TL Chris Hill
           TC Chris Hill
           TR Chris Hill
           BR Chris Hill

Page 71   TL Chris Hill
           TR Chris Hill
           BR Chris Hill

Page 72   TR Chris Hill
           BR Chris Hill

Page 73   TC Chris Hill
           TR Chris Hill
           BR Chris Hill

Page 74   TL Chris Hill
           TR Chris Hill
           BR Chris Hill

Page 75   TR Chris Hill
           BR Chris Hill

Page 76   Chris Hill

Page 77   TR Chris Hill
           BR Chris Hill

Page 78   Chris Hill

Page 79   Chris Hill

Page 80   TL Chris Hill
           TR Chris Hill
           BR Chris Hill

Page 81   TL Chris Hill
           BL National Museums
           Northern Ireland
           TR Crown copyright

Page 82   BL Crown copyright
           TR Chris Hill

Page 83   TL National Museums
           Northern Ireland
           BL Crown copyright
           TR Irish Salt Mining and
           Exploration Company Ltd

Page 84   Top Chris Hill
           Middle Chris Hill
           Bottom iStockPhoto

Page 85   Top National Museums
           Northern Ireland
           Middle Crown copyright
           Bottom Crown copyright

Page 86   Natural Environment
           Research Council

Page 87   Crown copyright

Page 88   TL Chris Hill
           BR Crown copyright

Page 89   Crown copyright

Page 90   TC Crown copyright
           BC iStockPhoto
           TR iStockPhoto

Page 91   TC Chris Hill
           BC Provided by Northern
           Ireland Environment
           Agency, Crown copyright
           TR Crown copyright

Page 92   Top Chris Hill
           Bottom Chris Hill

Page 93   Chris Hill

Pages 94   National Museums
and 95   Northern Ireland

Page 96   Chris Hill

Page 97   Derived from the
           1:500, 000 Bedrock
           Geological Map of Ireland,
           published by the Geological
           Survey of Ireland 2006

Page 98   Chris Hill

Page 99   Crown copyright

Back cover   Chris Hill

Every effort has been made to identify copyright holders. In the event of an error this will be rectified in future productions.